NIETZSCHE'S
FOOTFALLS

Published in Great Britain in 2001 by
GERALDSON IMPRINTS
25 Rutland Gardens, Hove, East Sussex BN3 5PD

Printed in Goudy 11 in Galicia by Ángel Lago, Imprenta A Moderna

ISBN 0 9514499 2 3

Goethe - The true sign of genius is a
posthumous productivity.

NIETZSCHE'S
FOOTFALLS

A triptych

David Pollard

In Wagner's tragedy 'Leubald und Adelaide', written while he was still at University, every one of the characters is murdered before the final act so that quite a few of them are forced to return as ghosts to allow the work to come to an end.

Nietzsche: Only the day after tomorrow belongs to me. Some of us are born posthumously

For Lucia

CONTENTS

Introductory

Röcken still lies in the Eastern German flatlands under a limitless cobalt grey sky and, because there are signposts pointing away but none towards it, you can easily drive past without realising it is there. The village is just off a road surfaced with cobbles that shake the car violently to a crawl. It lies beyond Lützen, site of the battleground where Napoleon defeated the allied Prussian and Russian armies on his victorious march to Moscow (a march another dictator tried later with equal success and equal failure). Nietzsche mentions that he saw cheering rebels passing the parsonage on wagons during the year of revolutions but the very rarity of this contact proves the isolation of the place. Off the road are the few houses that make up the village, children playing on bikes raising dust on the earth tracks. Like the motorway a few miles away and the great armies that on to their battle at Lützen, the world has passed the place by. It is not on the map and it is not easy to get off the motorway at the right place or to get back on to it again. Once there, the steeple directs you to the church and you leave the car in the shadow of a wall.

The place is run-down like the rest of the village. Surely no services have been held here for a long while. However, the latch moves down and, if shoved, the door gives.

Inside, the place has a quiet Lutheran beauty. Facing the east end are fifteen rows of wooden pews painted in pale red, green and white. A balcony runs around three walls and is painted with improving inscriptions from the Bible. Above the door is a small organ. In front of the apse is a wooden screen which incorporates altar, pulpit and vestry. The altar is painted and the pulpit, of the same design, is directly above it. The cross on the altar seems to point towards the place where the parson would stand to give his weekly sermon. The South wall has seven deeply set windows which throw a gentle shadowy light into the building. Like the motorway, time has passed this little building by. Outside, the surrounding churchyard is overgrown and full of weeds and high grass. This isn't really the kind of graveyard you expect.

There are only a couple of tombs and these, peaceful in the evening light, are set against the south wall of the little church. The more showy of these is covered in carefully raked pebbles and almost overshadows the three graves beside it. These are overhung with a soft green bower so as to make it difficult at first to read the inscriptions on the stones to the right and left. But you lean down and push the greenery to one side. The grave on the right, which is different from the others, is inscribed to Franziska Nietzsche born Oehler and the dates are 2nd February 1826 to 20th April 1897. The grave on the other side is dedicated to Friedrich Nietzsche, born 15th October 1844, died 25th August 1900. On this are some fading flowers, lobelia in a pot and a wilting bunch of cut irises. The stone in the centre, clear of the shadows, is altogether easier to see and belongs to Elizabeth Förster-Nietzsche, born 10th July 1846, died 8th November 1935. It is difficult not to get the impression that she has elbowed aside her mother and her brother in the calm of death.

The parsonage is a nondescript three storey building which is now in private hands and no amount of persuasion will get you into the room in which Nietzsche was born. The woman who answers the door, standing there with her hands on her hips, tells you that it is not possible although she hesitates for a moment at the mention of money. Here, as always, birth and death are within a few footsteps of each other but no hint of what brought the baby to the grave. The real posthumous existence is not that far away at Weimar where the mad philosopher lived quietly with his sister, saying little and writing less, while his reputation was both made and destroyed in the archive downstairs.

But this is only one story of posthumous existences, of real lives that have past. There is another which also has to do with graves. On the fifth of May 1934 Uberbahnsturmführer Alfons Sachs or Shacks and Gruppenführer Henrik Himmler (no relation) boarded the steamer SS Peru for the four thousand mile journey across the ocean to the coast of Latin America. Both felt honoured to have been chosen for this crucial mission. They had in their care a small urn; stone, Greek in form but without the subtlety, in which was some German earth. This they were instructed to take to the heart of the Paraguayan jungle. The urn had been sent half way round the globe for a ceremony dear to the heart of the leader of the Third Reich and Elizabeth Förster-Nietzsche, one of his most faithful subjects. Around a grave in the middle of an unkempt clearing a small crowd had gathered, composed mostly of the schoolchildren who are always commandeered for these occasions. The seal on the urn was broken and German soil, the real stuff from the fatherland, sprinkled over the grave.

After a delay of nearly half a century this gesture put an end to the half-and-half existence of the man whose body was and still is rotting beneath. Certainly he was dead and a valid certificate issued to that effect by the proper authorities and yet, in the old country, there was much hard work being done to resurrect both husband and brother

9

and turn them into... Resurrection that can qualify mortality and deny it its quiescence, that can make a corpse revolve a hundred and eighty degrees in its grave and face about. Certainly this is one of those deaths denied the finality hoped for in endings. His ghost is still there, hovering and dangerous.

No coincidence, perhaps, that the little ceremony by the graveside took place in Asunción. The town was named, of course, not after the assumption of Moses but of Mary who was gathered up into heaven to live in glory for all eternity. You know the kind of thing, clouds parting and the virgin, dressed in blue satin which shimmers in the light of sun and halos, floating upwards towards the figures of God and Jesus who sit on high, awaiting her with outstretched arms. The Paraguayan jungle mists swim and part just like the clouds in so many religious paintings and, as they do so, in the space that now becomes visible, the tombstone is revealed. The grave is now overgrown with weeds and began to fall apart many years ago. There is a cracked vase which is sometimes filled with flowers. On the headstone are words inscribed in the hope of a similar kind of resurrection, 'Here lies with God, Bernhard Förster, founder of the colony of 'Nueva Germania''.

But this is a strange kind of after-life where ghosts and zombies dwell, those half-dead who return to haunt us through the generations. The reverse of sanctification. There is an unpleasant smell of suicide in the air and a persistent refusal of the dead to lie still in their graves and of the living to leave well alone. The grave is in the cemetery of San Bernadino, named after a fifteenth century preacher monk who, for much of his life, ranted against the Jews.

Förster's death, the Paraguayan one, leaves another body in that parade of the dead. It took place in the Hotel del Lago, near the provincial capital. On the morning of June 3rd 1889, the maid as usual pushed her trolley loaded with sheets and towels along the corridor on the second floor and opened the door of the bedroom. The poor girl was half stunned by the smell of chemicals in the stagnant air. On the bed was the already stiffening corpse. She left it there and fled for help. Earlier Förster had written to his sister, 'I am in a bad way. What will become of us?' Then he had put the pen carefully on the little cabinet by the side of the bed and had swallowed a lethal mixture of strychnine and morphine.

This pathetic suicide lies at the centre of a subtle mixture of lives and resurrections. That of Friedrich Nietzsche for one. On January 3rd, exactly five months to the day before the discovery of that stinking body half way round the globe in Asunción, the philosopher had left his hotel room in Turin and made his way towards the Piazza Carlo Alberto where he saw an old nag being brutally whipped by its master. Overcome with pity for the beaten horse he had broken into tears, staggered across the square and flung his arms around the poor animal's neck in an attempt to protect it. Then he had collapsed sobbing onto the cobbles. Thus ended a prolonged period of euphoria and the beginning of his own posthumous existence. In Turin at that very moment, sitting at his desk, was Cesare Lombroso, the author of 'Genius and Insanity'.

The sister of the insane philosopher was the widow of the corpse in Asunción. She knew exactly where her duty lay and immediately fled from husband to brother, from one kind of posthumous existence to another. By the way, and this is also part of the story, it was Hitler, the German dictator, the one who tried to end the legend of the wandering Jew in his own original way, who sent the earth of Germany to cover that grave in the jungle of Paraguay. And this leads us to another resurrection, perhaps the most dangerous of all, the one which demands the final burial of the holocaust and the celebration of the führer's birthday half a century and more after another suicide, this time by a bullet in the head in the private bunker un-

11

der the burning city of Berlin. Then there is Heinrich Heine, the Jewish poet lying on his mattress grave and another, John Keats, who was the first to think of the phrase 'posthumous existence' to describe a life beyond the world in the very letter in which he makes his 'awkward bow' from it. 'I have', he writes far away from home and friends in Italy, 'an habitual feeling of my real life having past'. Both of these are dying and yet still alive. And it doesn't stop there, for there are infinite resurrections, each playing on the other till the end of time. These lines merely add to them, are yet another rebirth and remembering of things which need, perhaps, to be forgiven.

Thus we have a whole series of unquiet graves all of which are the legacy of Palinurus, the exiled pilot of Aeneas' storm-tossed bark who, chosen as victim to assuage the fury of Juno, was vanquished by the god of sleep and cut off from the boat he was steering, taking not only the tiller but the rudder and entire stern along with him. As Dryden translates the Aeniad, 'The God, insulting with superior strength / Fell heavy on him, plung'd him in the Sea, / And, with the Stern, the Rudder tore away'. This left Aeneas to fulfil the oracle and land, quite by chance or at least without the aid of his pilot, on the shore of Italy, the birthplace of fascism.

Palinurus, after 'Three blust'ring Nights', finally came ashore near Velia, only to be brutally murdered and left on the beach. Because unburied, he had to wait a posthumous hundred years before being permitted to cross the Styx. Incidentally, Dido called out for the same fate for Aeneas, 'Let him fall before his time and lie in the sands unburied'.

There was another unquiet grave, this time in a darkened room at number 50 Rue d'Amsterdam. Here lay the poet Heinrich Heine, the first Jew to achieve real prominence in the history of German letters. He was the son of

Samson and the grandson of Lazarus. Born before the wedding of his parents, he was, as well as being Jewish, also illegitimate. The Heine family business had failed and his father, just like Nietzsche's, had lapsed into a kind of epileptic madness, another kind of posthumous existence. He writes of a visit to his father, 'In my delight at seeing him, I wanted to rush up to him and kiss his hand. But strangely enough, the nearer I came to him, the more everything became blurred and changed its shape. When I bent to kiss his hand, I was seized by a deathly chill, the fingers were dry as twigs and he himself a tree without leaves and covered with frost'.

Likewise, Heine lay dying ever so slowly. In Germany it was announced that he had entered an asylum and, soon after, that he had died. This was near enough to the truth. In fact he had returned to Paris and taken to his bed, or rather a pile of mattresses in a shabby second floor room. A small ante-room led to this bedroom which was basic but large enough. The place was in semi-darkness and semi-silence, the curtains drawn, the only sound of piano playing which came from the other side of the courtyard beyond. The poet himself lay in a darkened part of the room separated from the rest by a screen. On the walls were a portrait of his wife and two etchings by Robert, 'The Fishers' and 'The Reapers', but they were hardly distinguishable in the gloom. On mattresses placed on the floor lay Heine. Once the visitor had got used to the darkness he could see the wasted body under the bedclothes. His beautiful, white, bloodless hands lay on the counter-pain and his face, also beautiful, showed no pain. His relief came, not from strychnine and morphine but from writing and morphine. He stayed immobile on this bed for eight years.

In these rooms he lived half helpless on his mattress grave, a posthumous existence which lasted just two years less than Nietzsche's. Both were controlled by adoring women jealous of their own role: Nietzsche by his sister, Elizabeth, Heine by his wife, Mathilde. The story goes that the poet's existence was little helped by her beha-

13

viour. The only doctor who ever relieved his terrible suffering was a certain Dr Wertheim. He bravely complained
about the quality of Mathilde's nursing and got punched
squarely on the jaw for his pains after which he never returned. She was horribly jealous of anyone who could do
more for the dying poet than she could herself.

An eternity with nothing to do. Hour after hour in the
company of drifting thoughts, trapped in a death once
removed, a body cradled in time, like a baby but without
the hope of escape, of getting up on uncertain legs and
walking away. Caught up in immobility surrounded on all
sides by thoughts that prey like vultures on one's own flesh,
thinking it already dead. Imaginary mirrors stare back in
every direction. Eyes, pallid in the half light and that
strange grin of the zombie which insists on the certainties
that have to be forgotten until the next thought rises to displace it and even that is the same thought. Idle time has
gates that swing too easily. The slightest draught blows
them open to admit large sorrows it had hoped forgotten.
Not vistas of daffodils under a blue sky but fears.

Fear, of course, is origin and out of that Hades came
his finest work. The poems he wrote at this time were
'like listening to a man buried alive', They are 'a cry
from the grave', a cry in the night from someone buried
alive, or even from a corpse, "Life is lost to me forever"'.
An unquiet grave, without the privileges of the dead, who
have no need to spend money and write letters, let alone
books, In this unhappy state, 'I've long been measured
for my coffin, and for my obituary also, but I am taking
so much time dying that I am beginning to find it as
tedious as do my friends'. 'I hope that the interminable
death song of the swan of the Rue d'Amsterdam hasn't
bored you too much!' whispered the sick man and turned away. When Mathilde prayed to God to forgive him
his unkindness, he told her, 'He will pardon me; it is his
job'.

Nietzsche thought very highly of Heine, 'The highest conception of the lyric poet was given me by Heinrich Heine. I search over the realms of thousands of years for equally sweet and passionate music in vain [...] and how he handles his German! One day it will be said that Heine and I have been far and away the first artists of the German language - at an immeasurable distance ahead of everything that mere Germans have done with it'.

Heine's illness can be dated from 1844, the date of Nietzsche's birth. In this year he published his 'New Poems' and 'Winter Story'. It was towards the end of that year that Heine's uncle Solomon died, a multimillionaire worth some 40 thousand million francs. Heine had always been led to understand that he would inherit a considerable pension from this estate but nothing was mentioned in the will and his cousin, Carl, to whom the fortune was left, allowed Heine a mere 2000 francs a year, a pittance. Heine was devastated, '>God forgive my family for the sins they have committed against me. Truly it is not the question of money, but the moral outrage that the most intimate friend of my youth and my blood relation did not honour his father's word that has broken the bones of my heart; and I am dying of the fracture'. The shock of his disinheritance weakened him in the face of his disease. He was threatened with jail if he should try to re-enter Prussia and went in-stead to Barèges in the Pyrenees where his health collapsed. He was almost blind and could hardly speak or swal-low and he had continual fainting fits. It was then that the announcement of his death was made and he lay down on his mattress grave. He had trouble with his eyes and his mouth and often could not swallow his food. He had to push up his left eyelid with his finger in order to read, 'Alas, I can now eat only on one side and weep only with one eye. Oh ladies, shall I be able to claim only half your hearts in future'? He could not even kiss.

15

That year then, 1844. A year we need to tread around with some care. A year with its own history which circles round its own and other stories. A few more pointers:

John Smith and his brother Hyrum, founders of the Mormon Church, were dragged from their prison cell by a mob of 200 and lynched in Carthage, Illinois, the result of a disagreement over the question of polygamy. A rioter commented, 'If the law could not reach them then powder and shot could'. Brigham Young rose up to be the new leader. The Smiths were translated.

James Knox Polk was elected the eleventh President of the U.S.A. Polk was president from 1844-1848. He began a process which doubled the size of the nation within a decade and gave the fledgling land some lebensraum. His stated aims were 'the reoccupation of Oregon and the re-annexation of Texas' and it was indeed during his rule that Texas was added to the United states. The U.S.A. and China signed their first treaty of Peace, amity and commerce. Joseph Buonaparte, brother of the dictator, died.

Much in the way of publications. Dumas Père produced both 'The Count of Monte Christo' and 'The Three Musketeers', Charles Dickens finished 'The Chimes' and 'Martin Chuzzlewit', Elizabeth Barrett Browning wrote her 'Poems'. A new and enlarged edition of Schopenhauer's 'The World as Will and Idea' appeared.

Also in 1844 Karl Marx, who Nietzsche never met or mentioned in his writing, met Friedrich Engels in Paris and wrote 'The Jewish Question'. This year also saw this descendent of a line of Rabbis married, exiled and converted to Communism. In his book, Marx explains how the Jews emancipated themselves through the power of money, 'The Jews have emancipated themselves insofar as the Christians have become Jews. Money is the jealous god of Israel, beside which no other god may exist. The

Christian has absconded with Judaism' and 'the social emancipation of the Jew is the emancipation of society from Judaism'. A curious twist for a Jewish anti-semite who writes of 'the stock-exchange synagogue of Paris' and of 'Stock-exchange Jews'. Bakunin wrote that 'this whole Jewish world which is made up of a single exploiting creed' is a world that is 'at the disposal of Marx on one hand and the Rothschilds on the other'. When the communist millennium finally arrived the Jews would, naturally, 'disappear'. It was Heine, of course, who wrote that 'money is the god of our time and Rothschild is his prophet'. Engles published 'The Condition of the Working Class in England'.

In the spring of 1844 Darwin began to jot down some notes of an idea that had been running around in his head. By the end of the summer it was a full 189 pages long. It was the first draft of what was to become, some fifteen years later, the first edition of the 'Origin of Species'.

In 1844 Gustave von Salomé married Louise Wilm in St. Petersburg. Later, they had a daughter. In the same year the Polka was introduced into Europe from Bohemia and Wagner finished and carefully revised the score of Tannhäuser.

And of course, Eugène Sue published his ' Wandering Jew'.

Also in 1844, Benjamin Disraeli published his novel, 'Conningsby', the first of his political trilogy, the other two being 'Sybil' and 'Tancred'.

Disraeli's uniqueness was to emphasise his Judaism in- stead of hiding it 'In spite of centuries', he wrote to his Christian readers, 'of tens of centuries, of degradation, the Jewish mind exercises a vast influence on the affairs of Europe. I speak not of their laws, which you still obey, of their literature with which your minds are saturated; but of the living Hebrew intellect. You never observe a great intellectual

17

movement in Europe in which the Jews do not greatly participate'. Disraeli went even further, 'On every sacred day you read to the people the exploits of Jewish heroes, the proofs of Jewish devotion, the brilliant annals of past Jewish magnificence. The Christian Church has covered every kingdom with sacred buildings, and over every altar [...] we find the tables of the Jewish law. Every Sunday -every Lord's Day- if you wish to express feelings of praise and thanksgiving to the Most High, or if you wish to find expression of solace in grief, you find both in the words of the Jewish poets'. In this Disraeli agreed with De Chirico who wrote in his Memoirs, 'Anti-semitism will end only when the Jews stop hiding and assuming the attitudes of whipped dogs and will say in a loud voice and to everyone's face 'I am a Jew and I am proud of it!'

And this is interesting because Disraeli really did believe, just like the anti-semites who followed closely on his heels, of a Jewish conspiracy of chosen men, of a chosen people dominating history from behind the scenes. In his first novel, 'Alroy', he writes of a plan for a Jewish Empire controlled by Jews and in 'Conningsby' there is still Jewish money controlling world diplomacy and governing the courts and governments of the world. Just like Hitler's publicity machine, Disraeli believed 'that the first Jesuits were Jews; that mysterious Russian diplomacy which so alarms Western Europe is organised and principally carried on by Jews; that mighty revolution which is at this moment preparing in Germany and which will be in fact a second and greater Reformation [...] is entirely developing under the auspices of Jews'. And even, 'all is race [which is ...] the key to history' and, 'there is only one thing which makes a race and that is blood'. Not only theory but practice. It was Henry Oppenheim who told Disraeli that the Khedive of Egypt wanted to sell the Suez canal and it was Lionel Rothschild who lent him the four million pounds to pay for it.

18   This did not go unnoticed. There was even a piece in

'Punch' by Thackeray, also in 1844, called 'Codlingsby' in which Mendoza, who is a direct descendant of Rebecca, reveals to The Marquis of Codlingsby that absolutely everyone is Jewish, including the King and the Pope. That same year, Christopher North, under the pseudonym of Professor Wilson, published an 'Anti-Conningsby.

A return to the question of fear and origin which is never far away. An internal resurrection which is at the heart of stories. Even Jesus had a problem with origins, born with some questions as to his paternity, he vanished for thirty years before reappearing to testify that he was the son of God.

Hitler is not much less of a muddle. His father, Alois, was an illegitimate son who grew up with his mother's maiden name and no guarantee that she knew who his father was. The story goes that after the death of his mother, he also vanished for some thirty years only to reappear to testify that he was in fact not a Schicklgruber but a Hitler. Would he have been taken as seriously if he hadn't changed him name? Much later, Nietzsche, in his turn, insisted on coming from a line of Polish aristocrats as his name, Niâzky, shows. He was to write, 'I am a pure-blooded Polish nobleman in whom there is not a trace of ignoble blood, least of all German blood'. His mother used to tell him and Lisbeth about their ancestor Count Nietzski who had defied religious persecution when he had been involved with the break from the Catholic church. As a result of his defiance he had been banished and had led a life of wandering from one place to another for three years, not quite as long as the eternal exile of the wandering Jew. Their son, born the night before their flight, had been brought up during their wanderings and this had given him the strength to resist all his ordeals. He grew up healthy and lived long and trans-

19

mitted both qualities to his heirs. Later Nietzsche was easily recognised as a Pole and this even by the Poles themselves who addressed him in Polish and expected a reply. One of them tells him, 'Your race is Polish, but your heart has turned heaven knows where'. In a letter to Gast from the spa at Marienbad, 'There are many Poles here and they - it's most extraordinary - insist on taking me for a Pole, keep greeting me in Polish, and refuse to believe me when I tell them I'm Swiss' and wrote, 'Personally, I am still so much a Pole that I would sacrifice all other music for Chopin'.

When Nietzsche told Cosima that he was descended from a line of Polish counts she answered, 'What a pity, I would find you much more interesting had you been the son of some unpretentious clergyman from Thuringia'.

Thus are things reborn. Origin and re-birth hover around the question of inspiration and the beginnings of stories. It is generally accepted that Heine's 'Tannhäuser' ballad was used as the basis for Wagner's opera. It has its name in common as well as its giants and dwarfs, Valkyries, a young Siegfried, elves and gnomes and all the population of German myths. The gnomes, who are called Nibelungen, mine for precious stones deep in the earth. They wear little caps which can make them invisible and forge the best swords which only the giants know how to use. It is even possible that Heine's 'Elemental Spirits' of 1837 gave Wagner the idea for 'The Ring'. The title of 'Götterdämmerung' dates from a Heine poem of 1832. No doubt about it. Wagner called Heine a talent ' which few in Germany can equal' and 'which with more favourable care would have attained to the level of the greatest names of our literature'. He was 'the great awakener of the German mind'. However, he was later hugely offended by Heine's 'Tom Cat's Concert for Poetry-Music' which was inspired by Wagner's theories about the relation of music and poetry. In part it runs:

> The Philharmonic Tom-cat's club
> Is starting to believe
> In artless Music, in its
> Fashion primal and naive.
>
> It wants poetic music now -
> Roulades, not quavers kissing,
> Poetry less instruments -
> A voice with music missing
>
> It wants the reign of genius, though
> It may botch things outright,
> But in the arts, oft unawares,
> It soars to the greatest height
>
> It honours genius that keeps
> To nature as its king,
> And doesn't boast great learning, as
> It hasn't learnt a thing.

It is hardly surprising that Wagner took objection to this and fell out with Heine as he fell out with Nietzsche. Heine was now a 'highly gifted poet-Jew versifying with the airs of true poesis. His wit he got from Voltaire, his style superficially stolen from other German poets'. A footnote to do with posthumous existences - Cosima, after her husband's death, controlled performances of his music with an iron fist. One result of this was to prove Heine right. Singing went out of the window and was replaced by declamation, 'the emphasis must be placed on the language'.

This still leaves the question of the 'Flying Dutchman'. Wagner had once acknowledged his debt to Heine's version of the story which is called 'The Memories of Herr

21

Schnabelewopski'. He wrote, 'The treatment of this Aha-suerus of the Ocean, taken by Heine from a Dutch thea-tre piece, gave me everything to hand'. However, by the time he came to write 'My life' in the 1860's no single word of this influence remains. Could this have been because Heine thought of the wanderer as a symbol of the eternal vitality of the Jews while for Wagner he represent-ed a kind of eternal zombie in search of redemption in a Christian world?

The original idea for the story came from a legend cur-rent on the island of Nordeney and it was Heine who sketched out a drama based on the legend after a visit to the place. This describes the curse on a sailor who has asked for the Devil's aid in rounding a dangerous cape and is doomed, in a horrible posthumous existence, to sail the seas forever. The Dutch captain refuses redemp-tion offered him by a series of faithful women and always returns to his ship to avoid marriage. He finally meets Katharina, the daughter of a Scots captain, but then, at a crucial moment in the plot, spots a girl in the audience with whom he leaves the theatre for an hour's dalliance only returning in time to catch the final few minutes of the action. This scene Heine added to the original leg-end. The captain is redeemed by the love of the adoring Katharina who calls out in a loud voice, 'I was faithful to you until this moment and I know a sure means of re-maining faithful unto death'. At these words she hurls herself into the sea and the curse of the Flying Dutch-man is lifted. He is saved and we see the ghostly ship sink-ing beneath the waves. However, Heine's treatment is certainly not tragic or even serious. His moral is that women should be careful not to marry flying Dutchmen and that men may come to grief through even the best of women.

Heine's treatment of the story is ironic and subtle yet there was something in this tale of the eternal outsider that caught Wagner's imagination, something that brought it into line with one of the recurring sub-plots of

European writing, that of the wandering Jew, a plot that had been endemic in European literature since the Middle Ages. It is mentioned in Germany by Goethe, Schubart, A.W. Schlegel, von Brentano, Chamisso and Gutzman, in England by Byron, Shelley and Wordsworth, and in France by Edgar Quinet, Béranger, Gérard de Nerval and Alexander Dumas. In 1847 Sue's book, published, as you will not have forgotten, in the year of Nietzsche's birth, was dramatised for the theatre and put on in 1851 at the Opera to music by Halévy. Earlier, in 1834, a journal had come out with the express intention of reporting the progress of this creature, 'The wandering Jew is the Jewish race, dispersed eternally amongst the nations, without merging with them, without becoming a brother to them, alone amongst the peoples of the earth, thus fulfilling the prophecies of the divine curse'. It is the tale of a representative of the Jewish people, driven into exile as an eternal punishment for their repudiation of Christ. Like Cain he had been sent to wander the earth for the murder of a brother. He was the Judas Iscariot of the western world, the man who betrayed Christ with a kiss, so unlike the kiss that Heine, in his own posthumous existence, was unable to give. And there he is even in O'Henry's story, 'The Door of Unrest', where Michob Ader turns up looking 'like Father Time's younger brother' who tells us, 'I saw Jerusalem destroyed, and Pompeii go up in the fireworks; and I was at the coronation of Charlemagne and the lynching of Joan of Arc. And everywhere I go there come storms and revolutions and plagues and fires. 'Twas so commanded'. Each individual Jew, a stranger in his adopted land, therefore, was cursed in the eyes of his Christian neighbours not because of anything he had done but because of what he was, exiled into himself from himself. No final catharsis to this story unless it be the state of Israel whose second biggest city is Los Angeles.

23

The Encyclopaedia gives us

Nietzsche, Friedrich (1844-1900) German philosopher. His first book, 'The Birth of Tragedy' (1872), argued that Wagnerian opera was the successor to Greek drama. Nietzsche rejected Christianity in favour of the "will to power". In 'Thus Spake Zarathustra' (1883-92), he praises the man who is free, titanic, and powerful, an ideal adopted by the Nazis. After 1889 he was permanently insane.

A few births and deaths to keep the cycle turning. In 1844, on 15th October, Nietzsche was born. In July 1846, Elisabeth Thérèse Alexandra Nietzsche was born. In February 1848 Joseph Nietzsche was born and the following September Karl Ludwig Nietzsche died mad.

His father, Karl Ludwig, was a minister of the Lutheran Church as were both of his grandfathers. One of these, Friedrich August Ludwig, rose to become superintendent. The mother of this superintendent had been born of a line of pastors which went back to the early seventeenth century. All the ancestors of both sexes were solid German citizens who had borne solid German names. Nietzsche was called Wilhelm Friedrich after the king of Prussia who was little more than a figurehead for Bismarck's ruthless regime which created the Greater Germany and, because of its industrial backbone and organising abilities, led step by step to the wehrmacht.

1848 was not only crucial to the life of Nietzsche but to Europe as a whole as it was the Year of Revolutions which saw serious rioting in fifteen European capitals. The bourgoisie hoped to gain a say in government. The trouble was that their example encouraged the working classes to show that they also had aspirations. This threat from below frightened the middle classes and they put themselves in league with the monarchies against the aspirations of the workers. It was the end of William IV's liberal leanings in Prussia. Both there and elsewhere new constitutions were imposed from above and, at the end of the day, the ruling families were stronger than ever.

1848 saw the meeting of the Frankfort Assembly which Marx called 'an assembly of old women'. They elected a regent in the person of Archduke John but talked themselves out of their jobs. When Schleswig and Holstein revolted against Denmark, Prussia came to their aid but was forced by the other European powers to withdraw its troops and sign the Convention of Malmöe. When Schleswig and Holstein then appealed to the Assembly they agreed to ratify the Convention and this resulted in an insurrection in the streets of Frankfort. Two deputies were murdered by the mob. The rising was crushed by troops from Austria and Prussia and any prestige which the assembly might have had was destroyed. They had lost the support of the people by calling on foreign troops to suppress a popular uprising. In this year a list of ministers was drawn up and Frederick William IV wrote beside Bismarck's name, 'Only to be employed when the bayonet governs unrestricted'.

History went on its jolly way. In 1849 Austria was excluded from the German Federation. It had taken half a century for the Germans to wriggle out from under the hegemony of the Hapsbergs. Frederick refused the Imperial Crown saying of himself that 'I am not a great ruler'.

The 'Convention of Olmütz' was signed in November 1850. Here Prussia agreed to the dissolution of the Union. Three years after the revolutions of 1848 Austria was still the dominant power in Germany. Germany had been worsted by Austria because of her weakness. She learnt the lesson. While the Austrian monarchy had been built by marriages, the Prussian monarchy had been built by the sword. Prussian instincts were military and it was now prepared to lean on its strengths. Bismarck wrote, 'Woe to

25

the statesman who in these days does not look around him for a reason for war which will hold water when the war was over'.

In 1861 William I succeeded to the throne of Prussia and the work of military reconstruction was seriously begun. His plan increased the standing army from two hundred thousand to nearly half a million. A year later, in 1862, the Prussian parliament refused Bismarck's proposals for reform of the military so he simply proceeded without their permission. Success silenced opposition. He wrote, 'We are a vain nation. We feel hurt as soon as we cannot swagger'.

War between Prussia with the aid of Austria against the Danes. We are in 1864. By the Treaty of Vienna Germany gained the Duchies of Schleswig and Holstein and the possibility of constructing a canal to the coast and creating a new destiny on the open seas.

In 1866, after working for two years to create the right conditions, there was war between Prussia and Austria. The conflict lasted just seven weeks and was, as Fisher summarises it, 'a revelation to Europe of the results which might be attained by the application of Prussian science and Prussian methods to the military art. The swiftness of the Prussian mobilisation, the precision of the Prussian movements, the excellence of the Prussian needle gun, the clever use which was [...] made of railways, portended the advent of an era in which the great decisions of history would be governed by the relative capacity of states to make use of their technical and scientific resources, and the direction of war would more and more resemble the management of a vast and intricate industrial business'. Or, to put it another way, Hanoverian muzzle-loaders against Prussian breech-loaders. The Prussians won the Battle of Sadowa against Austria and the minor German states which had sided with her. The Treaty of Prague created a

North German confederation under the leadership of Prussia which gained the Kingdom of Hanover, the Electorate of Hesse, a part of Hesse-Darmstadt and the city of Frankfurt. Bismarck knew where to stop and didn't demand the annexation of Austria which came somewhat later under a leader who didn't know where to stop. Austria was now excluded from German affairs and Prussia, with an increased population of some four million souls, was undisputed head of a North German Confederation. In the Bundesrat Prussia controlled only 17 of the 43 votes but the real power lay elsewhere. William I controlled the army and foreign policy so the Bundesrat could chatter as much as it liked. Moltke thought that 'The war of 1866 did not take place because the existence of Prussia was threatened, or in obedience to public opinion or to the will of the people. It was a war which was foreseen long back, which was prepared for with deliberation'.

Napoleon III of France had hoped that the Prussian war against Austria would be long and exhausting and that he would be called in at the end to act as arbiter and that France would control the entire area. He was shocked at the rapid defeat of Austria. Bismarck had now consumed Hanover, Hesse, Cassel and the two duchies and dominated all of Germany to the River Maine, had added four and a quarter million new souls to the population of his country and had overturned the whole balance of power in Europe. Still, he was convinced that 'a Franco-German war must take place before the construction of a United Germany would be realised'. Bismarck commented, 'Let us get to work. Let us hoist Germany into the saddle. She will soon learn to ride'.

He did not take long. In 1870 Napoleon III was manoeuvred into declaring war on Germany and this resulted in the Franco-Prussian war which had been so confidently predicted by Bismarck and in which Nietzsche fought as a medical orderly. Bismarck was convinced that only a foreign and nationalist adventure would unite the whole of

27

Germany while in France there was also a desire for a fight. Because they had not been humiliated in the war of 1866 Austria remained on the sidelines. The battle of Sedan was followed by the capitulation of Metz which was rapidly followed in 1871 by the Fall of Paris after a four month siege. Complete victory for the Prussians. The 'Peace of Frankfort' was in February. Germany gained Alsace and Lorraine, Metz and a huge indemnity. The southern confederation joined the North German Confederation. The armies of a united Germany with kings and princes at their head met at the heart of France. On January 18th Wilhelm I, King of Prussia, accepted the nomination of the German princes as Emperor of a united Germany and was crowned German Emperor at Versailles although the ceremony was not performed in a railway carriage and there is no record of his dancing with excitement afterwards. Thus the establishment of the first German Reich. The ceremony which took place in the Hall of Mirrors ended with the playing of the Prussian hymn 'Heil Dir im Siegskranz'. The music had been composed by an American, Henry Carey, and is now the British National Anthem.

When Bismark began his rule in Berlin. Germany was the most populous country in Europe after Russia and, even including Russia, the strongest. The Customs Union was already secure and political union and national sentiment soon followed. 'Was it unnatural that these Prussian patriots, throwing their minds back to the obscure origins of their state in a little military outpost of German speaking men in a sea of Slavs and seeing its ineluctable rise, should discern therein the workings of a peculiar and flattering providence? Was it unnatural that they should believe that the Prussian race, by its frugality, its hardihood, its stern application, its formidable and disciplined violence, was selected to accomplish an historic mission on earth. There were some even, who cast their minds forward and asked if there might not be a greater destiny reserved for them ...'

Bismarck, whose genius had brought all this about, had done so with the help and even friendship of the Jews and was now denounced for his dependence on them and for accepting their money.

The Paris Commune erupted while the country was in the hands of the Prussian army. The revolution in the capital was put down by soldiers of the defeated French army during the 'Bloody Week' in May in which 20,000 Parisians died. Thiers to the fore in founding the Third Republic because the royalist groups argued hopelessly among themselves. However, Bismarck knew where to stop. He had no wish for a great empire overseas or for expansion to the east. He never threatened England on the high seas. He didn't make the mistake of a later chancellor of Germany. He did, however, after two attempts on the emperor's life, pass a law against the socialists which placed the natural rights of the citizen under the heel of the police. Obedience was the watchword.

In 1876 Leopold II of Belgium was invited to Brussels for an international meeting of explorers and geographers to consider an expansion in the study of Africa and to work towards the elimination of the slave trade. This resulted in the Belgian Congo and the beginning of European colonialism. The Congo Free State was not free to the Congolese and freedom of trade allowed the place to be milked and its people enslaved in situ. Germany and others had to follow suit and within three years there were the beginnings of Germany's colonial empire. As the Germans could only think of their colonies as bits added onto the Reich, they could offer little more than slavery to the newly acquired conquests of the master race and thus they created furious antagonisms and finally failure.

Although Bismarck had already signed the 'Alliance of the Three Emperors' in 1873, a contract of mutual aid between Austria, Russia and Germany, he went behind the Tsar's back six years later and signed the 'Dual Alliance'

29

between just Germany and Austria-Hungary. Germany now had two conflicting alliances, the second designed to protect her against a signatory of the first.

In 1882 Italy joined the 'Dual Alliance' making it into another 'Triple Alliance' creating the axis which was there in readiness for the Great War.

In 1887, still afraid of a war on two fronts, Bismarck approached the Reichstag with a request for an army of 700,000 men.

1888 was the year of the three emperors and the end of Bismarck. Death of Wilhelm I at the age of ninety. Crown Prince Frederick, was never given the chance to be great, dying of cancer in as many days as the years of his father's reign. His liberal tendencies were never given a chance. The crown passed on to Wilhelm II. He ruled fifty million subjects and a united country that dominated the map of Europe. Germany dropped its pilot. Wilhelm was, to put it mildly, unstable and became increasingly bossy and theatrical, building crazy dream castles and listening to Wagner. He began to make speeches about 'shining armour'.

In the final ten years of the century Germany had doubled her production of both steel and iron. In the last twenty her steam tonnage had increased seven-fold. She had coal in the Ruhr and iron in Lorraine and a hard working people and was rapidly becoming the greatest industrial power of the world. She established colonies in West Africa, in South-West Africa, in East Africa, in New Guinea.

At the turn of the century something like 150 million people living in an area of some 10 million square miles were governed by one or other of the European powers. Nationalism was being backed up by colonialism and the Christian missionary. The flag and the cross.

25th August. Death of Nietzsche.

PART I
Wagner

The Encyclopaedia gives us:

Wagner, Richard (1813-1883) German composer. Name means 'Cartwright'. His father died when he was six months old and his mother married Ludwig Geyer nine months after that. His early operas, 'Rienzi' (1842) and 'The Flying Dutchman' (1843) led to his appointment as conductor at the Dresden Opera House where 'Tannhäusser' was successfully performed (1845). During the composition of 'Der Ring des Nibelungen', an operatic treatment of German mythology, he fell in love Mathilde Wesendonck (1828-1902), who inspired the opera 'Tristan und Isolde'. Wagner later married (1870) Cosima von Bülow (1837-1930), Liszt's daughter. In 1863 he produced "Die Meistersinger von Nürnberg' and began building a theatre in Bayreuth for the first performance of 'The Ring' (1876). His last opera, 'Parsifal', was produced in Bayreuth in 1882.

Nietzsche's compositions couldn't have been that bad. When Wagner was shown a piece for piano which he had

31

written, he expressed approval and demanded to see the composer. The introduction had come about quite fortuitously through a friend of the sister of his professor at Leipzig university. This professor was Friedrich Ritschl whom Nietzsche had followed to Leipzig from Bonn. Wagner was travelling around incognito as he often did and was staying with his friends, the Brockhauses, on his way through Leipzig. Nietzsche received an order to come to the house and meet the master in a tête-à-tête on the following Saturday. He duly made his appearance only to discover that Wagner had whisked himself off for another incognito meeting elsewhere. So incognito were Wagner's incognitos that they were incognito even to those in the know. However, there were apologies and cups of coffee all round and the fam-ily asked Nietzsche to return the following evening when there would be a larger party which it would be more difficult to disappoint. Nietzsche accepted and decided that he ought to dress up for what he assumed was going to be a more formal occasion. He was influenced in this decision by the fact that his tailor had promised to finish a new suit for him in time for the great occasion.

The day started out with snow and rain and Nietzsche's excitement could not be dispelled by his usual walk. The afternoon was spent with a fellow student discussing the place of God in philosophy but when dusk had already passed and there was still no sign of the suit he began to get worried. He went out to the tailor's and found the assistants working hard on his order which they assured him would be ready in forty-five minutes.

A little mollified, he walked over to a cafe and ordered a drink. There was a periodical on the table which he picked up. Glancing through it he read with some surprise that Wagner was away in Switzerland. This gave him a feeling of being involved in an intrigue. When he got home an hour later, there was still no sign of the tailor so he settled down to wait with a dissertation on Eudocia. Not long after, he heard noises outside. He opened the window and saw the tailor's old assistant standing at the gate below, grasping a packet under his arm. He yelled down through the rain that he should come up. The suit had arrived at last and it was time to get changed. Nietzsche tried on the suit and found it to be a perfect fit but the assistant had instructions to wait until he had been paid. Nietzsche was now very excited and told the man that he would only pay the tailor himself and not the assistant. However, the man stood his ground and refused to leave without the money. Time was now getting short, 'Finally, a show of dignity, a solemn threat, a curse on my tailor and his assistant, an oath of revenge. End of Act II. Myself brooding in a shirt on the sofa, wondering whether a black jacket is good enough for Richard. Outside, pouring rain'.

Thus he arrived in the charming drawing room of the Brockhauses with much excitement but no suit. Apart from the family, only Wagner himself was there. They were introduced and Nietzsche muttered a few compliments. Spurred on by this display of admiration and his own egomania, Wagner immediately asked how familiar Nietzsche was with his music. Then, hardly waiting for a reply, he began to rail against almost every production of his operas, the companies and their conductors. His energy and confidence impressed Nietzsche, 'He is a wonderfully lively and ebullient man, who speaks very quickly and is very witty. He makes such a private meeting quite cheerful'.

At the end of the evening Wagner shook hands with the young student. He offered to show Nietzsche's music to his sister and other relatives and invited him to visit again for a discussion on music and philosophy. Nietzsche had been visibly impressed and, on Wagner, people who were visibly impressed made an impression.

The friendship was helped by Nietzsche's move to Basle. In 1869 the chair of classical philology fell vacant and Ritschl recommended his number one student for the post. He was appointed ten days before receiving his doctorate, the youngest professor ever at Basle. In fact, 33

he was so young that the examiner often turned out to be younger than the examinee. Ritschl wrote, 'never have I known a young man [...] who became so mature so early and so young as this Nietzsche'. Eventually the university gave him his doctorate without either dissertation or examination. Nietzsche wrote to Rohde, 'We are certainly fate's fools. Last week I had the idea [...] of tossing philology into the antique junk heap where it belongs. Now the devil 'fate' tempts me with a professorship in philology'.

He converted to Swiss nationality and moved. One of the attractions of his new home was its proximity to Wagner's new home, Tribschen, on Lake Lucerne.

Tribschen was a large, square house which overlooked the lake. On his very first visit Wagner had decided to make the purchase. He began a new life there, being joined almost immediately by Cosima and her three children. Nietzsche was soon a regular visitor, often staying over weekends and holidays. He made the place a kind of second home. A room was put aside for him and the Wagner children were soon calling him uncle.

Tribschen was something else. A large square three-storied house which had been redecorated for Wagner in rococo style with a great deal of pink satin and masses of small cupids. In the drawing room were large busts of Wagner and Ludwig II, and an oil painting of Wagner, a Tannhäuser picture, and Genelli's 'Dionysus among the Muses'. Gifts from the king were displayed, including silver bowls, an oil painting and statues of Tannhäuser and Lohengrin. Wagner had converted one of the rooms into what he called his 'gallery' where he hung engravings and photographs of sequences from productions of his operas and a Buddha given to him by the Comtesse d'Agoult.

Wagner's egomania and exhibitionism were apparent in everything he did, in private as well as in public. At the second Christmas which Nietzsche spent at Tribschen he gave Wagner one of Dürer's prints, 'Knight, Death and

the Devil' which pops up every now and then in these stories and which Wagner probably mistook for a representation of himself in armour doing battle with his enemies. Nietzsche later gave the same print to Förster. Equivalence can be damning.

In the matter of birthday presents, however, Wagner outdid his young protégé. He put an entire orchestra on the stairs outside his wife's bedroom and perched above to conduct them in the 'Siegfried Idyll'. She remembers the present in her diary, 'In came Richard with the five children to put the score of his symphonic birthday present into my hands. I was in tears, but so was the whole household'.

A quick biography of Wagner

1813
22nd May. Richard Wagner born in the Jewish quarter of Leipzig to a police actuary and Johanna Pätz who had been the mistress of Prince Constantin of Saxe-Weimar-Eisenach. He was only five months old when the city was surrounded by the cannons of the patriotic forces trying to set the fatherland free from the French. 22nd November. His father and a sister died of the typhus brought by the armies.

1814
28th August. His mother married Ludwig Geyer perhaps just a little too soon for comfort. He became a very loving father.

1815
26th February. He got a half-sister (or sister) Cäcilie.

1816
The new family moved to Dresden where Geyer worked for the court theatre.

1821
Geyer died in September. Richard was at the deathbed and
recalled playing a couple of little tunes on the piano. Geyer's comment? 'Might he perhaps have a talent for music?'
But his mother decided instead that he should make something of himself and discouraged his theatrical interests.

1822
2nd September. Entered the Dresden Kreuzschule where he
was put on the register as Richard Geyer. One day a school-
mate keeled over and died and commemorative poems
were requested. Wagner's effort won.

1827
Took possession of a large collection of Geyer's books
which had been left to him.

1828
21st January. Entered the Nicolaischule in Leipzig when
he decided to call himself Richard Wagner and produced,
at some expense to his regular studies, a tragedy called
Leubald. This he tried to set to music. Had an early infat-
uation for Leah David, daughter of a Leipzig banker.

1830
The July revolution in Paris reverberated in Leipzig
where the students were on the march. Wagner joined in
with some relish. This gave him a taste for student life.
On to University in Leipzig as studiosus musicae. Saved
from a duel by the fact that his opponent was killed in
another duel earlier the same day.

1833
Was given the post of chorusmaster at Würzburg.

1836
4th November. Married Minna Planer, an actress who was
really a calm German hausfrau. She was lead actress in
Heinrich Bettmann's theatre company and he spent some
time following them around.

1837
Minna fled to her parents leaving him horribly in debt.
21st August. He arrived in Riga and took up a post there
as director of the theatre and stayed two years composing
Rienzi.

1839
Fled from his creditors in Riga and, after an awful journey
across half of Europe, arrived on 13th August, in London.
Soon left for Paris where he stayed, half starving but,
nonetheless, composing Tannhäuser.

1842
Rienzi accepted in Dresden where, on 20th October, it
was received in triumph. Wagner accepted the post of
Royal Kapellmeister for life. Security at last.

1844
Nietzsche was born and Wagner finished Tannhäusser.
And Eugene Sue... and Disraeli... and Schopenhauer...

1845
19th October. Tannhäuser produced at Dresden.

1848
The year of revolutions and Wagner was caught up in the
liberal ferment of the time even reading a paper on repub-
licanism in public. This made him a rebel against the
King of Saxony, the man he should have loved, the man
who gave him the post of Kappelmeister at the Royal
Opera House. Even so, he managed to keep his court appointment. Started to work on a poem about Siegfried, a
hero who dies for the cause of revolutionary socialism. In
March Lohengrin was finished.

1849
When the battle was taken to the streets, Wagner took fright
and scurried away to Weimar where Liszt was preparing to
put on Tannhäuser. On 19th May a warrant was issued for his

arrest and he had to slip away once again, this time to Switzerland where he had to stay for twelve years. Until 1853, when he started on Rhinegold, he wrote hardly any music, producing instead a torrent of pamphlets including 'Art and Revolution', 'The Artwork of the Future', the gigantic 'Opera and Drama' and, of course 'Judaism in Music'.

1850
Second attempt at success in Paris ended in failure. He returned to Zürich and published 'Judaism in Music' in the Neue Zeitschrift für Musik under a pseudonym.

1852
Christmas. Met Mathilde Wesendonck. Finished the Ring and had it privately printed.

1853
Got Otto Wessendonck to fund a trip to Italy. Began composing Rhinegold.

1854
Finished Rhinegold and went straight on to Walküre.

1855
Visit to London where he kept on with Walküre and gave eight concerts for the Philharmonic Society.

1857
Cosima Liszt married Hans von Bülow. Wagner at work on Siegfried. He completed half of the opera and then stopped. He didn't take up the Ring again for twelve years. Soon in love with Cosima.

1861
Visited the Wesendoncks in Venice and saw the death of his hopes in that area.

1862
Went to Dresden to visit Minna. She was ill and full of

forebodings that she would not see Wagner again. She was right.

1863
Began his affair with Cosima.

1864
3rd May. A visit from the secretary to the King of Bavaria whose master, Ludwig II, granted his protection to Wagner and lots of money. Returned to Munich with the von Bülows.

1865
Cosima had a daughter, Isolde, by Wagner.

1866
Found refuge in Tribschen. Death of Minna. Returned to Munich.

1868
1st June. Premier of Meistersinger conducted by Von Bülow. By the autumn he was with Cosima in Tribschen. Bülow says, 'If it had been anyone but Wagner I would have shot him'. 25th July. Birth of Siegfried.

1869
Republished 'Judaism in Music' under his own name. 15th May. Nietzsche's first visit to Tribschen where unfortunately Wagner was working. Invited to return a couple of days later on Whit Monday for lunch. He soon became a member of the household.

1870
Cosima divorced von Bülow and married Wagner. Nietzsche was present at the first performance of the Siegfried Idyll on the staircase at Tribschen on Cosima's birthday, Christmas eve.

1871
First visit to Bayreuth.

1872
22nd May. Wagner's Birthday. Laying of the foundation stone for the new theatre which would have highly raked seating and a sunken orchestra pit.

1873
Move to Bayreuth.

1876
13th - 17th August. Bayreuth opened with a performance of the Ring.

1877
Visit to London to raise money to pay off the debts of the Festival Theatre. There the composer, along with Hans Richter, conducted eight concerts at the Albert Hall. He also read 'Parsifal' to Queen Victoria. Cosima confided to her diary, 'All Israel is working against us'. Later in the year he was composing 'Parsifal'.

1882
The Parsifal Year. 26th July. First performance of Parsifal. Something quite new. Wagner asks, 'Can a drama in which the most sublime mysteries of the Christian faith are shown upon the stage be produced in theatres like ours, in front of audiences like ours, as part of an operatic repertoire like ours?'

1883
13th February. Died in Venice

The Wagner myth was created as much by Cosima as by Wagner himself. The perfect wife for the monomaniac, she was able to keep up her side of most conversations and was also prepared, indeed revelled in, his endless monologues. She treated him as much like a god as it is possible to do on this side of the grave, worshipping him to the point of hagiography. She kept his eyelashes about her, carrying them around as if they were some kind of holy relic. So much better to be idolised by an attractive, intelligent disciple than one with fewer qualities. Above all she was devotedly reliable and efficient, always struggling on his behalf, acting as his secretary, organising his household, answering his letters and screening those who asked to see him. Like a chief minister she had put herself in his service but, also like a chief minister, she revelled in the power the position gave her.

She was not averse to angling for money to advance his plans. When Ludwig allowed him a grant of some 40,000 florins, his officials at the treasury, who were hell-bent on hindering the scheme, thought up a really good wheeze to obstruct their royal master. When Cosima came to collect the donation, they placed before her a huge pile of sacks containing the money in small coins. Without flinching, she personally loaded them into the carriage with the aid of her maid and drove off. Both before and after his death she worked tirelessly for him.

Just as Elizabeth did for her brother. In fact the parallel between the two women doesn't stop there. When Elizabeth wrote about Cosima and Wagner she did so without realising, or only half realising, that what she was writing might just as easily have applied to herself and her brother. As follows, 'Cosima was the personification of will-to-power in the noblest sense of the term. As long as he lived she exercised influence by and through him by which I do not want to imply that she ruled him, only that his art, his fame, his greatness and his puissance were the instruments of her power. It is only since his death, or so at least it seems to me, that his illustrious gifts have been given the fullest expression. To judge Cosima by any other standards would be to misunderstand her splendid character, her abandonment of Bülow for Wagner, her entire rich and full life and her later development into the "Margravine of Bayreuth"'. Only a couple of words need to be changed.

41

An odd story in reference to Geyer. The question of the geier or vulture which impregnates the Wagner story. Nietzsche had himself suggested a vulture for Wagner's coat of arms which he wanted for the title page of his latest theoretical piece, 'On Conducting'. At this time Nietzsche was still enthusiastic enough about Wagner and Tribschen to agree to Wagner's constant demands upon his time, demands which he found very difficult to meet due to the pressure of his own work. Wagner wrote to him, 'The coat-of-arms turned out very well; we have every reason to thank you for your meticulous care. But here my old vulture draft has risen anew, the bird of prey that everyone takes for an eagle until told that scientifically there is such a thing as a 'cinerary vulture,' closely resembling the eagle. Now since, because of the relationship, the 'vulture' absolutely has to be recognised at once; may we ask you to prevail upon the engraver to give our bird its characteristic ruffle - using any available picture of the beast'.

Nietzsche agreed and co-opted an all too willing Elizabeth in the hunt for a picture. She, however, unlike her brother, was annoyed that there would be no proud eagle on Wagner's crest of arms. It was Nietzsche who divulged to her that the reference was to Wagner's paternity. And there was another myth about vultures, an Egyptian one, to place in this story of myths, that procreation by a vulture is possible without male intervention. The vulture is thus a fatherless bird, a bastard, and this leads us neatly to a coda, a tail, as we might now naturally mention Freud's interpretation of a vulture's tail placed in the mouth of the baby Leonardo da Vinci as the male organ. This meant that 'he had had a mother but no father', or that he was a child 'who was aware of his father's absence and found himself alone with his mother'. Leonardo, like Wagner and also Cosima, was illegitimate.

It was not only the request to correct the image of the

vulture on Wagner's coat of arms that came to Nietzsche from both Wagner and Cosima but a hundred other demands. Too many of Wagner's letters were demands, some of them for the most trivial things. When Hans Richter was at Tribschen to help with the orchestration of 'The Ring' Cosima wrote, 'Dutch herrings are greatly in demand...' When Nietzsche was ill after the fighting in 1870 it was more of an inconvenience to them than a concern. These herrings also needed his expert attention.

But Nietzsche was being reserved for even greater things and was soon co-opted as philosopher to the court of King Wagner. His first book, 'The birth of Tragedy out of the Spirit of Music', was, in the final sections, a deep and submissive bow in the direction of the maestro. It was, until section sixteen, an academic study of Greek drama showing how Socrates, in league with his friend Euripides, managed to kill off tragedy as the genuine embodiment of the dionysiac and irrational abysses in apollonian form replacing it with a new one which was later spotted and defined by Aristotle and which was rational and philosophic, theoretical, a view of tragedy which governed the form down the centuries until ...

These early sections were based on lectures he had given at Basle two years before that first meeting with Wagner. Sections 16-25 are tacked onto the end. Here the argument is a grovel. If Socrates and Euripides destroyed the music of pre-tragic drama then a new master was needed to return it to its original place. Magistra ex machina. This 'German spirit is still alive, and in marvellous health, like a knight who dreams far underground in an enchanted sleep. From out of these depths rises a Dionysiac song, letting us know that this German knight is still dreaming of the ancient Dionysiac myth in his blissfully serious visions [...] One day the knight will find himself awake in all the morning freshness of his immense sleep. He will slay dragons, destroy the cunning dwarves, rouse Brünhilde, and even Wotan's spear will be unable to bar his way'. Wagner gobbled this up along with his breakfast to put him in the mood for composing.

43

Nietzsche suppressed his own thoughts at the bidding of his admiration for the master. He writes of 'the huge task I had to perform for Wagner and which really provoked many and weighty contradictions within me'. He was incredibly sycophantic and wrote to Wagner about the Birth of Tragedy, 'On every page you'll find me trying to thank you for all you've given me, and the only doubt that plagues me is whether I've always received it properly'. And again, 'I would rather tell you in person how many purely scholarly problems have been gradually clarified for me because of your absolutely unique and memorable personality'. He tells Gersdorff that Wagner 'is filled with such an absolute idealism, such a profound and moving humanity, such a sublime eagerness for life, that when I'm in his presence I feel I'm in the presence of the divine'. A man with his forehead on the ground, Nietzsche had become Wagner's 'literary lackey'.

One more piece of help from the serviceable writer after the 'The Birth of Tragedy'. The new theatre got into endless financial difficulties which the usual appeals to royalty had failed to alleviate so Wagner decided to call on the German people to pull it out of the mess. Nietzsche was asked to write a call to arms for the project. He produced his 'Manifesto for the Germans' in which Wagner is called the 'great, courageous and indomitable champion of German culture'. This he took with him to Bayreuth where a visit to the building site had been arranged in the hope of encouraging the visitors to put their hands in their pockets. Unfortunately, it poured and Nietzsche lost his new hat to the Bayreuth cause. After the visit he read them his manifesto which they loudly applauded and then rejected. They accepted instead one less strident in tone. Rejection not from Wagner but from the Wagnerians.

Wagner even considered making Nietzsche legal guardian to his only son, Siegfried, so that he could watch over his education. Wagner hoped at one point that Nietzsche would give up his professorship for a time in order to assist in the preparations for the festival at Bayreuth.

But there were rumblings of discontent. As early as 1873 Nietzsche had had the temerity to leave the score of Brahms 'Triumphlied' on Wagner's piano in Bayreuth which led to a furious argument. Wagner couldn't stand Brahms either as man or musician and there is little evidence that Nietzsche liked him much either so this action must have been malicious. He sat at the piano and played bits from the score in Wagner's hearing and, when one of the maestro's retinue removed it, Nietzsche found it and put it back. It was a large score with Brahms' name in huge letters across the cover and every time Wagner came into the room the hated name was there glaring up at him from his piano. Eventually this led to words, Wagner apoplectic and Nietzsche pale faced and silent. Nietzsche must have sublimated the experience until it exploded years later in his anti-Wagner outbursts of 1888.

Two years later there occurred a telling little episode recalled by Elizabeth. Cosima had written to Nietzsche asking him to send his sister to Bayreuth to look after the children for weeks on end while the two parents went off on their travels. This Nietzsche obligingly did, writing to his sister and asking her to help them out. She went to Wahnfried with presents from 'Uncle Nietzsche' and stayed after the return of Wagner and Cosima. She wrote in her diary, 'I shall never forget the quiet evenings when the children had been sent off to bed and we sat together in the library talking of all manner of things. At first my brother was the chief topic of conversation and I can still see the significant looks exchanged between Wagner and Frau Cosima as I related how cheerful my brother had been during the Christmas holidays and how many diverting things he had to tell about the Basle circle, "Then why does he always write us such melancholy letters?" asked Wagner almost angrily, "Does he do that?" I replied, genuinely astonished and, upon receiving an affirmative answer, hastened to explain that, in writing to Wahnfried,

45

he was always made to realise how far away he lived and could no longer share all their intimate family experiences as in the good old days at Tribschen'. Wagner seemed somewhat mollified. She remembered later her careful caressing of the maestro's ego.

More rumblings. Nietzsche sent Cosima a piece for violin and piano. She wrote of it, 'I once received 'New Year's Bells' in Tribschen. I sat down and played. Jacob Stock, who was then my butler and would always say to me through the various vicissitudes of life, 'One just has to be fin,' stopped setting the table, listened attentively, and finally turned away with the words 'Don't like it'. I must confess that I laughed so hard I couldn't play any further'.

Cosima certainly saw in Nietzsche a useful tool in her drive to create the Wagner myth. But as soon as she suspected that Nietzsche was not behaving like a true courtier, she began to treat him with disdain. It was quite natural for her to look down her nose at people, being taller than a good many of them.

After all that, another question asked by Nietzsche in 'The Case of Wagner', 'Was Wagner German at all?' A question which is not as strange as it may seem at first sight, 'Great learner that he was, he naturally learned to imitate a great deal that was German, but that is all. His very soul contradicts everything which until now has been thought of as German; not to speak of German musicians!' 'It is', he writes, 'difficult to find any German peculiarities in his character'.

One step further and Nietzsche is maintaining not only that Wagner may not have been German but that might even have been a Jew. Both Wagner himself and his official biographer said that his father was Carl Friedrich Wagner, a petty police actuary from Leipzig. Nietzsche tells us that Wagner had confided to him that he was really the son of his step-father, Ludwig Geyer, a Jewish actor and painter. Ernest Newman, in his Life of Wagner, after carefully sifting all the evidence, comes to the same conclusion.

The relationships are, on the surface at least, fairly straightforward. The story is as follows. Friedrich, Wagner's father, adored Schiller and was an avid theatre-goer and amateur actor and these activities led him into the company of Ludwig Geyer. This Geyer was a man of some ability. He painted, wrote poetry and even a comedy called 'The Murder of the Innocents'. For much of his life he earned his living as a portrait painter and had the reputation of being an able musician. Wagner's father, Friedrich, died of Typhus when Wilhelm Richard was only six months old. Nine months after that his mother, Johanna, married Geyer and, until his mother was left a widow, the boy carried the surname of his new step-father who seems to have been a loving parent. Geyer was obviously very fond of the boy, more so than of the other children and called him 'the cossack'. Wagner remembered happy moments later in his life and even repeated them to Cosima who jotted them down in her diary. Geyer died when the boy was eight and Wagner tells of the three hour trudge to be at the dying man's bedside. Wagner is a Cartwright, a wagoner, Geyer a vulture. Wagner's name is, therefore, already a second coming.

During his time in Paris Wagner was invited to breakfast with Halevy for whom he was doing some paid transcription work. Present were several journalists all talking with the composer in French which was his mother tongue but which Wagner spoke hardly at all. At one point Wagner said a few words to Halevy in German to which Halevy responded. The journalists were surprised and told Wagner that they hadn't realised that Halevy spoke German. Wagner's reply was, 'Oh, didn't you know? All Jews can speak German!'

Do we sense just a soupçon of the fear of contamination here? German, like the geier, are touched with the bug of Judaism and are both of them to be driven away and distanced.

There is another Geyer, the last human being to whom Bela Bartok confided. This was the violinist Stefi Geyer to whom the first two movements of his violin concerto were dedicated and which includes the five note subject which he called Stefi's leitmotiv. In 1907 he told her that, although as a child he had been 'a devoted Catholic', he had become 'a new man - an atheist'. He called himself 'a follower of Nietzsche', an atheist who was striving for 'the highest degree of indifference'. Is this the result of 'Thus Spake Zarathustra', both that of Nietzsche and of Strauss?

This question of paternity, of origins, refuses to die and inhabits the dark corners of so much of the Wagner story. An oddity which, of course, has nothing whatsoever to do with the fact that Geyer was Jewish. In 1912 a certain Otto Bournot did a doctoral thesis on the question of Wagner's paternity. Delving into the Saxon parish archives, he worked his way right back to Wagner's great-grand-step-father, Benjamin Geyer who, lo and behold, had been organist at the Church of Eisleben at the end of the seventeenth century. Not a single one of this family that had not been a member of the Evangelical church. Thus the Geyer step-paternity contained 'nothing unfavourable'. Whew! Forget the assumptions behind such research that it accepted more of the step-paternity than it may have wanted. Anyway, the jokers who dubbed Wagner 'The Rabbi of Bayreuth' should have kept their pens in their pockets. But perhaps better to follow, not Heine's uncle but another Solomon, another Jew who had written some three millennia before of things which were too wonderful to be understood. One of them was the vulture in the sky.

Was Wagner schizophrenic with regard to this stepfather? On the one hand he wrote a loving memoir to him. On the other he treated Jews along with other enemies as threatening, as if they were extensions of the castrating stepfather, the uncle Claudius, who made his way into his mother's bed. On the one hand the man to whom he owed his life, on the other the man he had to suppress, the Jewish intruder. This threat had to be controlled and as soon as it escaped from this control it became a threat again. Nietzsche was surely one of the primary examples of this, loved while under the total sway of the master but hated when he had made his escape.

On Wagner's sixtieth birthday the celebrations included a performance of Geyer's 'The Murder of the Innocents'. In Wahnfried, his house in Bayreuth, he had a picture of Geyer on the wall.

Wagner's megalomania met with a string of failures. Why? Because performances of his music were being contaminated by compromises forced on him by theatre managements and Jews. He had grumbled about it for years. His tirade on that day in Leipzig when Nietzsche first met him had been on this theme. He now came up with a solution; to build a new theatre to his own design in the little town of Bayreuth in Bavaria, a place which was judenfrei and where he could control everything himself. The family moved from Tribschen to their new home, Wahnfried, at Bayreuth. Nietzsche paid his final visit to Tribschen between the 25th and 27th of April 1875 where only Cosima had been left behind to do the packing. On Wagner's birthday 22nd May, Nietzsche shared Wagner's carriage when he   rode into the town to lay the foundation stone for the new theatre. Nietzsche describes the moment, 'The stone

49

was laid [...] in the midst of the pouring rain and under a darkened sky. Wagner drove back with us to the town; he was silent and seemed to be gazing into himself with an expression not to be described in words [...] We know that at times of exceptional danger or, generally, at any decisive turning point in their lives, men compress together all they have experienced in an infinitely accelerated inner panorama'. That evening Wagner conducted Beethoven at Bayreuth and Nietzsche met Malwida von Meysenbug who remained friendly with both composer and philosopher.

The following year he wrote to Malwida after Christmas at Naumberg, 'Yesterday was the first day of the year. I looked into the future and trembled. Life is dreadful and hazardous. I envy anyone who is well and truly dead'. Various posthumous existences were fructifying around this time. Wagner had submitted to the Wagnerian. The great period was over. Nietzsche's subservience to Wagner was shuddering to a close and a great time of creative sickness was beginning which lasted until the uncreative existence of the asylums and the villa Silberblick. And Elizabeth met Bernhard Förster at Bayreuth.

The last letter which Nietzsche wrote to Wagner accompanied a copy of 'Human All Too Human' the tone of which is anti-Wagnerian if not anti-Wagner. Cosima immediately understood why the break had taken place, 'Israel intervened in the shape of Dr Rée, the Jew, very polished, very cool, apparently wrapped up in Nietzsche and dominated by him, although outsmarting him' - the relationship between Judaea and Germany in miniature.

Wagner himself took a different line. He put it about that Nietzsche was mad. He even went to the length of writing to Nietzsche's doctor suggesting that his sickness was the result of too much masturbation. With this Nietzsche was not well pleased. Neither was Elizabeth who, bearing the same name, was no longer an acceptable figure at Bayreuth. She was pulled both ways. Towards her brother in one direction and towards Bernhard and Wagner in the other.

The first of all the first nights at Bayreuth. Three separate performances of the whole of 'The Ring'. Nietzsche was present for part of the first but gave away his tickets for the second and, by the third, was back in Basle. When Lou Salomé spoke of Nietzsche at Wahnfried, Wagner left the room in a huff demanding that he should never be spoken of again in his presence. Another posthumous existence. 'The Wagnerian had become master of Wagner'. Wagner had become Teuton and anti-semite.

Nietzsche had escaped from the scene with Rée.

What did the master look like?

Paley tells us that, 'like other great men, he was short of stature, but neither stumpy nor dwarfed' and, he continues, 'His forehead was immense, and the whole expression vivid, decisive and commanding'. Elizabeth's description of him at Tribschen, 'He was dressed in a Flemish painter's costume consisting of a black velvet coat, black satin knickers, black silk stockings, a light blue satin cravat tied in a costly bow, with a part of his fine linen and lace shirt visible below, and an artist's tam-o'-shanter on his head, which was at that time covered with luxuriant brown hair'. But let's be fair. Wagner suffered badly throughout his life from an itchy skin complaint called Erysipelas and couldn't stand rough material to touch him. This explains in part his wardrobe of twenty-four silk dressing gowns. In part.

Wagner's creativity was always enhanced by his setting. He needed his satins and velvets, tulle and lace and silks. The first thing to be done when Wagner moved house was to create an environment in which he could work. He would dress himself in satins and silks and install himself in a room hung with drapes in soft colours. Once he had the public purse at his command he didn't stint himself. In the house at 21 Briennerstrasse, a present from King Ludwig II, his luxurious habits quickly became offensive

51

and later, at Tribschen, he created a temple to himself; a museum to his muse. Elizabeth, on her first visit to the house, noted that the decorations were 'disagreeably extravagant with its pink satin and cupids'. At the end of his life, while composing 'Parsifal', he had a secret correspondence with a French Jewess, Judith Gautier. He had become infatuated with her at Bayreuth during the second Ring cycle. He asked her to send him perfumes, bath essence and silks to help in the task. She did. They had the required effect and, tiring of the correspondence, he handed it over to Cosima who accepted the job, apparently with no hesitation.

Unlike Nietzsche, the publicist in Wagner loved being painted and photographed. Especially surrounded by a tastefully arranged collection of sycophants. Occasionally even an equal was permitted. Franz Liszt was allowed to sit at the piano. Cosima gets special treatment. Little idea is given by these images of the man's stature. Musically gigantic maybe but physically small. In a photograph with Cosima he gazes down into her admiring eyes, towering head and shoulders above her, an effect obtained by seating her in a chair and leaving him standing.

He appeared to Renoir in a black velvet gown with sleeves of thickly padded satin and the famous painter did a sketch of him. Wagner said that it made him look like a Protestant pastor. Nietzsche's father, of course, was a Protestant pastor.

Royalty was fascinated by Wagner. Ludwig II of Bavaria was spell-bound. He called Wagner his 'Friend and Only One, the fount of all rapture, my one and all, embodiment of my bliss, divine one. My mission is to live, fight, and suffer for him'. Ludwig was a neurotic princeling, brought up by tutors. His father, Maximilian, was a disciplinarian. It was feared at court that the young man would lose himself in a private world of dreams and be unable to carry out his duties as king. In 1861 he begged his father to arrange a performance of Lohengrin and was brought to the verge of hysterics by the effect it had on him. In the Hohenschwangau he strolled to and fro in rooms lavishly decorated on his orders with paintings of Siegfried and the Teutonic pantheon and, as he did so, his mind echoed with the words of Wagner's preface to the poem of the Ring in which he dreamed of a prince who would build a theatre dedicated to real German music drama and ended with the words, 'Would such a prince ever he found?' Indeed he would. Indeed he had.

When Maximilian died Ludwig was only eighteen and a solitary whose dreams were the same as Wagner's. His father's fears were realised. Hating all the panoply of state and everything to do with politics, he nonetheless had a dream which was as political as any, if impractical, a dream of ends without means, a dream of a regeneration of German culture (reach for your gun) through German theatre. Wagner wrote an essay at the king's request. It is called 'The State and Religion'. Here the composer describes the king's 'mission'. It is 'so uncommon' as to be 'almost superhuman'. If the ordinary man were to be faced with such a mission he would commit suicide, but a king 'is rescued from this consequence by the exalted earnestness of that inner ur-knowledge of the world essence which has become the standard of all his beholdings. At each instant he is prepared for the terrible phenomenon. And it is art that is his vital aid in this task'.

The young man spent his time strolling in the Bavarian Alps, dreaming his dream. It is an interesting reminder of the theme of madness that Newman, seeing things from a Wagnerian perspective, writes of Ludwig that 'he exhibited so many signs of exceptional sanity that it was a foregone conclusion that the world would some day declare him to be mad'. When Wagner was forced out of Munich it is hardly surprising to read that he took it to be the machinations of 'Jesuits and Jews', of 'the Jewish German masses (those horrors)'. Ludwig wrote him a note in which he called out 'Heil! to my beloved friend'.

53

However, Wagner always had the interests of number one at the centre of his plans so, when the war with France in 1871 left the Prussians in control of a regenerated German empire, he discarded the insignificant little king of Bavaria and turned instead to Berlin. Here was where the real power and influence now lay in the persons of Wilhelm I, Kaiser of a newly united country, and his chancellor, Bismarck. Wagner's patriotism, stoked by Cosima, knew no bounds. Plans for productions of his operas and for the national festival theatre veered northwards and went to Berlin, bypassing Bavaria. Ludwig, left out on a limb, now turned to building as a means of satisfying his theatrical impulses. He proceeded to construct a series of rococo follies in the Bavarian mountains in the name of German artistic regeneration. Inverted shadow of Speer. Inevitably Wagner turned to building as well.

A site for the theatre was found at Bayreuth and an announcement made that it would be opened in 1873. It would be darkened, have an unlit, hidden orchestra pit below stage and steeply raked seats, a bit like a proto-cinema. The burgers of the place were thrilled even though they already had a wonderful opera house which boasted the largest stage in the whole of the new German empire but this was quite unsuitable for Wagner's grandiose schemes. Old opera had to be by-passed and new opera had to be rebuilt from the ground up.

Although, perhaps, not quite so new as all that. Years before, at his first appointment in Riga, Wagner had worked at the opera there, a building which had three peculiarities: it was dark, it had stalls that were raked up like an amphitheatre and an orchestra pit which was sunk and almost invisible. A germ in the mind for later?

Wagner left Tribschen for Bayreuth in 1872. The foundation stone for the new theatre was laid on his birthday, 22nd May, with Nietzsche in attendance and Liszt staying away. They moved into their new house, Wahnfried, a name which means peace from torments, madness, illusion and fantasy. The design for the sepulchre to house them in their posthumous existence was finalised at the same time.

Wagner met both Bismarck and the Kaiser. Bismarck invited him to his private house. Cosima notes, 'R is absolutely delighted by his genuine, unforced kindness, no hint of reserve, a light voice, the most delightful communicativeness, exuding trust and sympathy'. Unfortunately, however, Wagner realised that, 'I will not be able to win his support for my cause'. For the Kaiser he gave a concert which was all his own work plus Beethoven's fifth. One of the incidental items was a Kaisermarsch. This was a big hit with the Kaiser who had it repeated again and again. But no help in coin from that direction. So, a new decision, 'The expenses of my enterprise will have to be borne by private persons'.

Circles of patrons, the Wagner Vereine, were organised to achieve this end. They consisted of private persons who were expected to contribute to the scheme. The idea was that each member would purchase one ticket valued at 300 thalers. Those who could not afford so much joined anyhow and purchased a ticket between two or three. One of the purchasers was Nietzsche. These groups were not too successful and Wagner soon discovered that the contributions were nowhere near covering the costs of the festival and, on top of that, their members expected him to feel obligated for their munificence and even conduct the occasional concert for them. Neither sufficient money nor sufficient subservience. In 1876 he cursed the vereine roundly and demanded their liquidation.

So still no money. The vereine had let him down. The German princes, who might have helped, preferred to put their money into 'Jewish or Jesuit undertakings'. Who saved the day? Ludwig. 'No, no and no again! It will not

DAVID POLLARD

55

end thus; help must be given! Our plan must not fail!' Ludwig was the 'wise fool who was needed'. Bavaria paid the crucial balance into the festival's capacious pocket specifying that the money was a loan and should be repaid. The surprising thing is that it was, mostly by Wagner's heirs out of the profits made by the festival.

Ludwig had come to the rescue and earned himself a special private performance of the Ring. The king arrived secretly by train and met Wagner for the first time in eight years at a signal box in the middle of a field. The performance left the usual impression, 'You are a God-man who cannot fail [...] the true artist who has, by the grace of God, brought down from heaven the holy flame to inspire, ennoble and redeem us on earth'. The Kaiser arrived three days later to a public welcome. Cheering crowds. He couldn't manage to sit through the whole of the cycle and left to supervise military manoeuvres. It must be noted that Nietzsche also fled but that, unlike the kaiser who survived two whole operas, he managed only two acts.

Later Hitler, another Wagnerite of a more menacing variety, would stay for the entire cycle. August Kubizek writes in his book about Hitler's youth, 'From the very first moment that Wagner entered his life, his genius had him in its grasp. With incredible tenacity and will-power he immersed himself in his life and works. He had experienced nothing like it before. He identified entirely with Wagner's personality. His heart beat faster as he read everything that he could find about the master, whether good or bad, admiring or critical. He was especially interested in biographical work, scribblings, letters, diaries and even the Autobiographical Sketch. He dug ever deeper into Wagner's life'. Adolf had no greater desire than to get to Bayreuth, the national shrine of German music. 'He sought for much more than a model and an example in Wagner. He literally appropriated Wagner's personality as if he needed to make it an integral part of his individuality'. His book, 'Mein Kampf', had some superficial similarities with Wagner's 'Mein Leben' apart from the title which was clearly an influence. Both of these books were dictated. Wagner's largish one to Cosima who acted as amanuensis. Hitler's little one to Hess, his gaoler at Landberg who wrote that, 'All day long and late into the night the typewriter would be tapping and one could hear him in his little room dictating to his friend Hess. On Saturday evenings he would generally read the completed section to his fellow prisoners who sat round him like schoolboys'. Incidentally, the book was typed on paper sent to him in prison by Winifred Wagner. In his 'Table Talk', Hitler divided the people of his epoch into Wagnerians and those who had no special name.

Of course, with all this reading, Wagner's anti-semitism must have rubbed off. Is not Hitler's anti-semitism much like Wagner's? Hitler's hatred of Jews can possibly be traced back to those couple of years when he lived in poverty in Vienna and had to sleep in a doss-house, Wagner's to a different couple of years of neglect in Paris. Both suffered destitution at a formative moment of their lives and both, in their megalomania, blamed the Jews. They were both nurtured as sons of the petty bourgoisie who so often saw the Jew as the cause of their misfortunes. Both were later resurrected as the genius of their epoch but failed to overcome their earlier hatreds. No point in thinking of these men's notion of revolution in your liberal democratic sense, one which seeks to free the world from bourgeois capitalism. For them revolution was centred on the hope that 'Germans and only Germans were able to lead the world to freedom and deliver it from [...] the taint of Judaism'. For them Judentum meant not simply Judaism, not even Jewishness but the Jews themselves. This menacing certainty is so often there in German revolutionary tracts and especially those written by Wagner and the führer.

German anti-semitism springs from a long history of Jew hatred which began as the Church emerged from secrecy into open acceptance in the Roman Empire and the story of Judas Iscariot, the betrayer of Christ, the disciple who bears the name of the Jewish people, began to find its way into the original gospel texts. John Chrysostom was one of the formulators of the doctrine, 'Where Christ-killers gather, the cross is ridiculed, God blasphemed, the father unacknowledged, the son insulted, the grace of the Spirit rejected'. The dichotomy is clear, 'If the Jewish rites are holy and venerable, our way of life must be false. But if our way is true, as indeed it is, theirs is fraudulent'. Christian and Jew share a Bible. If the Christian interpretation of the texts is correct then the Jewish one must be false. This is the basis of medieval anti-semitism. German enlightenment anti-semitism is embedded in this hatred and merely adapts itself to the loss of religious belief. In fact German anti-semitism is deeply embedded in German idealism from its beginnings in Kant. Here is the old master being critical in quite the wrong sense, in 'Religion within the Bounds of Reason Alone', hidden away in a foot-note we can find, 'In its original form, the Jewish faith was merely a collection of statutory laws over which was established a political organisation; as whatever moral additions were then or later appended to it in no way whatever belong to Judaism as such. Judaism is not really a religion at all but merely the union of a number of people'. Later, in a note to the 'Anthropology', he adds a few more comments and creates what has been called by someone who has not opened his Chaucer or his Luther among so many others, 'the most anti-semitic page in world literature'. Here we go again, 'The Palestinians [...] have [...] earned a not unfounded reputation for being swindlers because of their spirit of usury since their exile'. The Jews are 'a nation of cheats [...] the great majority of whom [...] seek no civil dignity and try to make up for this loss by the advantage of cheating the people among whom they find refuge and even one another. [...] They make the slogan "let the buyer beware" the highest principle in their dealing with us'. He tells us that they are traders because of their history and that 'it cannot be considered a curse [...] but a blessing especially since their per capita wealth is probably greater than that of any other people of the same number'. Unfortunately Christianity has 'certain sacred writings in common with them' and thus 'their constitution cannot be consistently abolished'. Here already is the German attitude to the Jews, a people lacking all that is self-evidently good, 'love, reason and freedom' and could, therefore never be good human beings. They were, above all and quite self-evidently a people who had rejected the very course of history and had failed to collapse quietly into oblivion like all other ancient systems of belief once it had performed its essential task and given Christianity to the world'. Saul Ascher understood the danger of an anti-semitism that thought itself to be 'rational and noble-minded'.

Fichte takes up the torch, 'In the breast of almost all the European nations there spreads a powerful state goaded by hostile feelings which is continually at war with all the others, and which in certain states dreadfully oppresses the citizens. I speak of Judentum'. These people 'are bar-red [...] from our meals, from our pleasures, from the affectionate interchange of well-being from heart to heart'. They are 'condemned to petty trading which weakens the body and shuts off the mind to all noble feeling'. And he adds, in case you are still in any doubt, that these people are so dangerous that they threaten the very core of civilisation and must be annihilated. The Germans must take over the role of chosen race from the Jews.

A follower of Fichte, Jakob Fries, who was professor of philosophy at Jena, called for the 'extermination of this Jewish commercial caste'. Of course he didn't mean it literally. He was speaking merely of a 'metaphorical, not a practical, extermination'.

Not practical but philosophical, an inner change was called for. On to Hegel who tells us that, although Jud-

59

aism had been crucial to the march of history, it had been superseded by its antithesis, Christianity and its state taken over by Rome. The Jews should thus accept the facts and give up their separate existence and assimilate into the world that they had been instrumental in creating. Hegel unfortunately died before he could explain how the Jews had managed to survive against the great sweep of historical inevitability but, nonetheless, driven up against this wall, Hegel began to see in Jewish stubbornness something more like 'admirable firmness' and publicly called for the protection of Jews during the Hep-hep riots but the young Hegelians didn't take any note of these later 'ramblings'.

Ludwig Feuerbach and Bruno Bauer took this all one stage further and Bauer's pupil Karl Marx continued the process. Where Feuerbach speaks of the Jewish God as being 'the ego of Israel', Marx writes of a more practical egotism, the desire of gain, of power and of cash. The Jews were the perfect metaphor for capitalism, indeed had survived in spite of history, had 'maintained and developed itself through history, in and with history'. The development of Jewry 'is to be perceived not with the eye of the theologian but only with the eye of the man of the world because it is to be found, not in religious theory, but only in commercial and industrial practice.' The Jewish Question was no longer a religious question but had a secular, real basis for 'once Jewry was stripped bare of its religious shell and showed its empirical, worldly, practical kernel, the practical really social way in which this kernel is to abolished may be indicated'. Of course a practical problem is that much easier or possible to deal with than a strictly religious one.

Thus can we read a supplement to the great sweep of German idealism.

And even at the very beginnings of humanism there is Luther. Luther! What constipation there was amid the avid flow of your thought. Did you ever hope that it might lead to . . ? 'Know Christians, that after the Devil you have no enemy more cruel, more poisonous or more violent that a true Jew'. These creatures should be punished because 'they hate the divine law in their very hearts and, as is the way with all hypocrites, they habitually condemn others. These are precisely the people who hate God's goodness, and pile up the divine wrath by their hardness of heart'. Cosima notes in her diary that 'in his thoughts Richard always lives with Luther' and 'feels related to him in many ways'. And, of course, Luther was Hitler's favourite reading.

Nietzsche's attitude to the Jews as if seen in a mirror.

Before leaving Naumberg in 1866 he placed an advertisement in the 'Leipziger Tageblatt' for a new room in order 'to get away from the Jews'.

Adulatory letter to Wagner hailing him as Schopenhauer's spiritual brother. Very sycophantic letter which praises Wagner for his awareness of the spiritual world which 'we poor Germans have lost in the night through every possible kind of political misery, philosophical mischief and Jewish pushiness'.

Disparaging remarks in some of his letters from Leipzig also. A few days after the French surrender to Bismark, Nietzsche wrote, 'So far not everything has been destroyed by Franco-Jewish trivialization and "elegance"'.

For Christmas 1871 Elizabeth asked for a book on the history of art by Springer but Nietzsche sent her one by Lübke instead because he would have had to order the other from 'a scandalous Jewish second-hand bookshop'.

Karl Mendelssohn Bartholdy, son of the composer asked Nietzsche to spend Easter 1871 with him in Greece. Cosima wrote, 'The son of Felix! This is very strange. I think I know what your decision will be'. He refuses.

The very day that he broke with Wagner was the day that he broke also with his anti-semitism. On 27th August of 1876, after his visit to Bayreuth where Wagner

was busy with rehearsals for the Ring, he left with Paul
Rée who was a Jew. At the beginning of October of the
same year he was at Veytaux with Rée who wrote that 'it
was the honeymoon of our friendship'. Cosima says that
the Wagners didn't discover that Rée was Jewish until
five months later but Nietzsche couldn't have kept the
friendship of both parties. His acceptance of Rée was his
dismissal of the Wagners and their anti-semitism.

At St Moritz in May 1877, he read a book by Siegfried
Lipiner called 'Prometheus Unbound'. Rohde had called
him 'the most bow-legged of Jews' and Rée said that he
was 'not an appetising creature' but Nietzsche wrote, 'If
this poet is not a "genius", I no longer know what genius
is'. And, in a letter to Lipiner, 'Tell me honestly whether
in respect of origin you have any connection with the Jews.
The fact is that I have recently had many experiences
which have raised in me the highest of expectations from
young men of this origin'.

In 'Human all too Human' he wrote of the Jews, 'in so
far as their energy and higher intelligence, their capital
in spirit and will accumulated in a long school of suffering from generation to generation, must come to prepon-
derate to a degree calculated to awaken envy and hatred,
so that there is gaining the upper hand in almost every
nation - and the more so the more nationalist a gesture
the nation is again adopting - the literary indecency of
leading the Jews to the sacrificial slaughter as scapegoats
for every possible public or private misfortune'. Nietzsche
agreed that the Jew has 'unpleasant, indeed dangerous,
qualities' and even agreed with Marx that 'the youthful
stock-exchange Jew is the most repulsive invention of
the entire human race' but he continued, 'Nevertheless
I should like to know how much must be forgiven a
people who, in a total accounting and even though not all
of us are to blame, have had the most grief-laden history of
any people and whom we have to thank for the noblest
human being (Christ), the purest sage (Spinoza), the might-
iest book and the most effective moral code in the world'.

In 'Beyond Good and Evil' he wrote of 'anti-Jewish idiocy' as an infection, 'Let in no more Jews [...] Thus commands the instinct of a people whose type is still weak and unresolved, so that it could easily be erased, easily extinguished by a stronger race. The Jews, however, are beyond all doubt the strongest, the toughest and the purest race living in Europe at present; they know how to prevail under the worst conditions [...] The Jews could [...] predominate if they wanted [...] but it is equally certain that they are not planning and working towards that end [...]rather they want and wish to be absorbed and assimilated by and into Europe, [...] to be respected and put an end to the nomadic life, to the 'Wandering Jew'. One ought to pay attention to this inclination and impulse and go out to meet it'.

In a letter to Overbeck, late in 1885, 'Generally speaking, there are good reasons for distrusting the anti-semites. By the way, their cause is more popular than one thinks it is from a distance; it appears to be warmly embraced, particularly by the whole Prussian nobility'.

'I see, by a decree of the Leipzig city council, that war has been declared on garlic - this is the only form of anti-semitism which smells good to your old cosmopolitan rhinoceros'.

According to Förster, Christ and the Jews are opposites, 'Christ appeared among the Jews because, on the dark background of the most depraved of all the nations, the bright figure of the Saviour of the world could stand out the more impressively'. For Nietzsche, however they were identified, 'Jesus and Saul are perhaps the two most Jewish Jews who ever lived'. And, 'Christianity issued from Judaism'.

Nietzsche's attitude to Förster's anti-semitism is clear. He wrote to Elizabeth after her engagement, 'Through this absurd step which you have taken [...] you show too clearly that you wish to sacrifice your life, not to my exalted aims, but to the ideals which I have gone beyond and must now fight against. You have gone over to my Antipodes [...] I will

63

not hide from you that I consider this engagement an insult - or a stupidity which will hurt you as much as me' [...] 'In all my reproaches you may trace my pain at having lost you, at seeing your name connected to a party with which I have no ideas in common' [...] 'For my personal taste such an agitator is something impossible for closer acquaintance'.

Elizabeth herself spoke of her husband's anti-semitism and tried to combat the idea that the Paraguayan colony had anything to do with it, 'the anti-semitic party did nothing whatever for my husband's colony'. But Nietzsche replied, 'You say that New Germany has no connection with anti-semitism, but I know for certain that the colonising scheme is fundamentally anti-semitic. I know this from the 'Correspondenzblatt' which is circulated in secret and sent to only the most trustworthy members of the party. (I hope your husband doesn't show it to you, it's becoming increasingly unpleasant)'.

Nietzsche later complained of this accursed anti-semitism which 'spreads its shadow over my entire existence. It has led to the fact that Wagner and I have become enemies and is the reason for the radical break between me and my sister'.

Writing before she leaves for Paraguay he calls himself 'an incorrigible European and anti-anti-semite' and Förster the organiser of a movement which is three parts bad [...] There can be no question of reconciliation with a vengeful anti- Semitic goose'.

Writing to her in Paraguay he told her he was pleased that 'this species of men [...]exile themselves voluntarily from Europe'.

In another letter there he wrote, 'One of the greatest stupidities that you have committed - for yourself and for me - is your connection with an anti-semitic chief which expresses a foreignness to my entire way of life which fills me again and again with anger and melancholy [...] It is a matter of honour with me to be in relation to anti-semitism absolutely clear and unambiguous, namely opposed, as I am in my writings [...] My loathing of this party is as outspoken as possible'. He complained that his name and writings were being used in anti-semitic tracts and that this 'has already made me almost sick several times'.

And, he added, 'in vain do I seek among them for some sign of tact, of délicatesse in relation to me. From Jews, yes; never yet from Germans'.

He called Georg Brandes 'the most intellectual Dane of the day - that is to say, a Jew'.

He mets Helen Zimmern and wrote, 'of course, she is a Jewess; it is amazing to see the extent to which this race now had the spirituality of Europe in its hands'.

Again 'Those who we call German musicians, especially the greatest, are foreigners, Slavs, Croats, Italians, Netherlanders - or Jews'.

And again, 'Our new Emperor grows more and more to my liking. The latest thing is that he is setting his face strongly against anti- semitism'.

To sum up, 'Once more in dealing with my whole attitude towards anti- semitism and the anti-semites. I can find a good deal to say in their favour, as there are many among them deserving of all respect, efficient and strong-willed people. Yet this does not prevent me from waging war upon anti-semitism - no, rather it forces me to fight a movement which dissipates and weakens so much vital power'.

In the margin of his last letter to Burckhardt he scrawled, 'abolish Wilhelm, Bismark and all anti-semites'.

He grumbled that 'Goethe was always offensive to Germans. He had honest admirers only among Jewesses.

His last note to Overbeck ended, 'Just now I am having all anti-semites shot'.

It might be worth noting that a man who is a convinced anti-anti-semite from birth is one thing but being raised in anti-semitic surroundings and changing his mind quite another. Just the opposite of Wagner who, before the appearance of 'Judaism in Music' showed not the slightest sign of anti-semitism.

65

Another note. Nietzsche's hatred of the Germans may have had something to do with their persistent lack of interest in the masterpieces he was producing. He had to publish many of his manuscripts at his own expense including 'Beyond Good and Evil'. In the case of the final part of 'Zarathustra', he paid out for four hundred copies of the text but a year later only seventy had been sold. When his publisher, Schmeitzer, was close to bankruptcy he put Nietzsche up for sale - for 20,000 marks - but could find nobody brave enough to take him on.

Another anti-German Friedrich and Nietzsche's favourite poet was Hölderlin who also ended up by himself in a little room in the house of Zimmer the carpenter. He would also have visitors who were welcomed as Your Highness or Your Majesty and were received with continual bows and other signs of deference. His room was also on the first floor with a window giving out over a wonderful view. He also trumpeted the glories of the ancient Greeks and denigrated the Germans writing that the Germans were 'always barbarians, made more barbarous by industry and science and even by religion, profoundly incapable of all divine emotion, corrupted to the marrow, so that the heavenly graces cannot but pity them; offensive in every degree of exaggeration and wretchedness, they are insensible to every finer spirit and without harmony like the shards of a discarded vessel'. In Germany 'You see handymen, but no men; thinkers, but no men; priests but no men; masters and servants, young and old, but no men. Is it not like a battlefield, where hands, arms, and other limbs lie around in fragments as the spilt life-blood oozes away into the sand'. And the conclusion of all this, 'I wished to leave Germany again and sought nothing further amongst these people. I was offended enough by intractable humiliations and did not wish my soul to bleed to death amongst such people'. In spirit at least he left to roam, a wanderer who another lover of Lou von Salomé called a 'wandering, most wandering, spirit [...] you only move as the moon does'. Poor poet, for his soul did bleed to death among such people but at least his tower was guarded by the good Zimmers.

Thus Nietzsche's break with Wagner was as much to do with his thinking as with his music, for Wagner was also a 'thinker'. Alongside the music he published his collected works. Carl Glasenapp wrote a hagiography of the man which came out in 1876 and treated his writings as seriously as his music. He was presented as a good man surrounded by sinners who knew not his worth. Not long after, Houston Stewart Chamberlain, who became the ideologist at the court of widow Cosima and married her daughter, Eva, called him one of the regenerators of the Nordic world.

Surprisingly Wagner was not at first an anti-semite. There is nothing before the appearance of 'Judaism in Music' that hints at the furious tantrums which were to come. He had perfectly normal relations with numbers of Jews. One or two examples, perhaps, stand out. During 1838 he was in debt to a Jewish moneylender by the name of Gottschalk who demanded to have his money back. Wagner threatened to take him to court but amid all the acrimony never once mentioned his Jewish origins. Again, there was the relationship with Moritz Schlesinger, a music publisher who employed Wagner to correct proofs. The great maestro in waiting must have rankled under this kind of paid labour and referred to Schlesinger as a scoundrel and frequently grumbled quite violently about him in letters without, however, once mentioning that he was a Jew. Then came 'Judaism in Music', written in 1851 under the pseudonym of K Freigedank which means 'free thought' a book which has been called 'arguably the seminal text of modern German anti-semitism' and, at the time of its publication, was almost entirely without parallel and thus yet another proof of Wagner's amazing originality. Wagner changed his mind about the Jews just like Nietzsche but in the opposite direction. From that moment until his death Wagner hardly wrote a single piece or had a single conversation which was not riddled with abuse of the Jews. When he was worried about payment for this anti-semitic tract he asked the publisher whether he would ever get his money, 'Forgive me asking this Jewish question but it is the fault of the Jews that I have to count every penny'. Even his Jewish friends and helpers were not free from this almost lackadaisical censure. Bernhard Löser is called 'the touching Jew Löser'. A Mr Seligsberg who sent an apostle tankard which Wagner craved is called 'the indispensable Jew Seligsberg'. It only needed something to go wrong for this to turn into open vehemence. Anything which he found unpleasant in a Jew was instantly attributed to his 'tribe'. For Wagner, the Jews were the direct cause of everything that was wrong with the world, 'industrialisation, banking, the press, in fact, the whole of modern civilisation'. Jews were not capable of creative activity in any field. Because people 'involuntarily want nothing to do with men of such appearance'. They are not suited to the profession of acting. They cannot write poetry because it always ends up sounding foreign. As for the field of music, any of their attempts at composition are horribly distorted by their background which includes the chants of the synagogue. 'Who is not seized by feelings of horror and ridicule, when he listens to such gurgling, yodelling and prattling which confuses our sense and our minds?' The whole of European culture, including its poetry and its music was foreign to the wandering Jew who must remain forever unattached to the 'natural soil, the true folk soul', from which all real art springs. And then we get inevitably to Mendelssohn, Meyerbeer and Heine. Mendelssohn's music is for entertainment only and can never reach to 'the deep and genuine feelings of the human heart'. Our fancy may in-

deed be effected but 'the innermost purity of human year-
nings for a clear artistic vision are scarcely touched'. The
fact that he never manages any 'heart or soul stirring
effects' is assumed and never demonstrated least of all why
it should spring form Mendelssohn's Jewishness even
though it is admitted that he had 'a fullness of talent [..]
the finest and most varied education', etc, etc. The same
for Meyerbeer, this 'Jewish operatic composer' but without the compliments. Meyerbeer is said to have treated
the opera house as if it were a synagogue not minding the
constant chatter while the performance was in progress.
For Heine the praise returns along with the paradox.
Here, as with Mendelssohn, we have a brilliant mind, one
which even went as far as to criticise Jewish musicians,
'his fellow musical tribesmen' and yet 'deceived himself
into thinking he was a poet'.

Is there any more that can be said about this mere
theorising which reached out and touched the music?
Well, there is always Beckmesser in 'Meistersinger' who
turns out to be the stereotype of the Jew of Wagner's
essay. He is limping, shambling, blinking, cunning and
devious and, of course, incapable of expressing himself
properly in German. He hobbles about the stage and his
gait is mirrored in the music. When he steals the prize song
he destroys the metre and garbles the text, unable to match
the music to the words. Beckmesser is a bass yet often he
sings as a kind of whining heldentenor. And then there is
Mime in 'Siegfried' who is left to the side of the scene
making trivial interjections as he cooks eggs in tin pots
while centre stage there is our hero belting out heroic
sentiments to heroic music as he forges a sword of steel.

And, just in passing, there is another question involving
the relation of the great works of art which the writer of
this diatribe was producing at the same time. There is
even an answer here, too. In 'Parsifal' there is the sacred

69

blood of the grail, the pure blood of a Christ of German descent, blood of the German spirit which was desecrated by the outsider. He called it a 'staged festival of consecration'. No, Wagner's philosophy is embedded in his operas. Hitler's attitude to 'Parsifal'? He saw it as a deeply racial opera, 'an absolute experience [...] the only thing that anticipates what I have to do'.

But someone has overheard all this ranting and at this point there is a creaking of the floorboards, a trap door flies open and a head pops through. It is Heine's and he is reciting his poem 'The God Apollo'. This tells of a nun who falls in love with Apollo and desires nothing else but to find the source of the divine music which she hears. She searches over the whole world and eventually finds the singer she seeks. Her Phoebus is none other than Rabbi Faibusch who is cantor of a synagogue in Amsterdam and who comes from the humblest of stock. His father is responsible for circumcisions and his mother sells pickles and second-hand trousers in the markets. For Heine the outsider, it is the schlemiel, the pariah, who is the creative artist and can make heavenly music on his lyre. This Apollo is not gurgling or yodelling or prattling but singing divine music. As Hannah Arendt points out, 'It is no longer the outcast pariah who appears the schlemiel but those who live in the ordered ranks of society and who have exchanged the generous gifts of nature for the idols of social privilege'.

Back to Wagner and some more yodelling and prattling. The German must avoid social intercourse with the Jew because it 'would mean the end of us Germans'. Nietzsche, on the other hand, calls 'anti-Jewish stupidity' an infection, 'Let in no more Jews [...] demands the instinct of a people whose type is still weak and undetermined'. In other words, the Germans.

At Wahnfried one of the most welcome visitors was the Comte de Gobineau who had written an 'Essay on the Inequality of the Human Races', a book which culminates in a paean of praise for the Germans. It is called 'Art and Inequality'.

Wagner got progressively worse under the influence of Cosima who encouraged his anti-semitism along with a piquant stew of nationalism and xenophobia. The Wagner circle was always talking about the Jews, 'The Germans are being used and ridiculed by the Jews'. This has made them lazy and undermined their trust and faith'. Brahms, whom he hated anyway, was of course turned into 'a Jewish Czardas player'. Wagner even encountered Jews in his dreams. In one he was molested by two importunate Jewesses and in another he was met at the door of a synagogue by two threateningly large Jews. In one of Cosima's nightmares he was even murdered by a Jew.

Wagner's anti-semitism surfaces like flotsam from some deep part of the ocean and is left rotting and visible on the shore. He writes, 'Our blood is corrupted by mixing the heroic blood of the noblest races with that of one-time cannibals. I regard the Jewish race as the born enemy of pure humanity and everything that is noble in it; it is certain that we Germans will go under before them, and perhaps, as a man loves art, I am the last German who knows how to stand up to the Judaism that is already gaining control of everything'. He rants on against Meyerbeer as the typical Jewish composer. In which way? Again as a man without a mother tongue, as an exile from the true core of language. As a man concerned merely with the rhetorical surface of speech. Where was he in respect of 'the march of opera music's evolution?' He 'followed this march, and never kept abreast of, to say nothing of outstripping, it'. A plagiarist, 'Not one departure is his own, but each he has eavesdropped from a forerunner and ex-

71

ploited with monstrous ostentation'. And why? For fame. To place his ladder on the platform of success and rise up it step by step'. No interest beyond that. Peculiar inability to see the beam in one's own. Wagner, of all the great composers was most interested in fame and money.

Wagner's attitude to Meyerbeer had not always been so very hostile. Indeed, earlier it had been one of love and admiration. In 1839, when they first met, Meyerbeer was the uncrowned king of opera in Europe and did a great deal to help Wagner when he arrived in Paris ready to take his first steps in the world of music. Both Meyerbeer and his wife not only lent him money when he was a down and out in Paris but helped him to penetrate the influential musical circles of the city. Later Meyerbeer put on 'Rienzi' in Dresden even though it had been refused as 'unfit for Germany' at both Munich and Leipzig. He also arranged for 'The Flying Dutchman' to be put on in Berlin. Wagner was effusive, he called Meyerbeer his 'adored protector' and wrote, 'Don't let them criticise Meyerbeer. I owe him everything'. He compared Meyerbeer to Handel and Mozart and wrote that 'It would be most inappropriate of me to break out in awkward eulogies of your genius, only so much as to say that I saw you entirely solve the problem of the German who made the qualities of the Italian and French schools his own and the creations of his genius universal'. He also thought that 'Meyerbeer retained his German heritage, the naiveté of sentiment, a chaste inventiveness' and even 'an unblemished conscience'. Indeed, in some of his letters things even get a little out of control in the submissive department, 'Neither my head nor my heart belong to me any more [...] I have to be your slave in body and soul [...] for I readily confess that my nature is to be slavish'. He wrote to his benefactor what he soon forgot, 'I will never be able to say to you anything but thanks and thanks again'.

72

And, indeed, this effusiveness changed dramatically. Meyerbeer became a man 'whose very smell repels me at a great distance'. He decided that it was Meyerbeer who had organised the critical attacks against him, 'This fury assumed more of the character of slander and malice, for in the meantime the movement against me had been reduced by Meyerbeer, a great connoisseur in such things, to a clearly defined system, which he upheld and practised with a sure hand'. Against these attacks Meyerbeer calmly turned his other cheek just as Lou von Salomé did later against similar libels made against her by Elizabeth. Wagner rejoiced at Meyerbeer's death, breaking into 'boorish laughter'. Meyerbeer, of course, sounds just a little like Geyer.

Incidentally, Heine also turned against Meyerbeer allegedly because he had not been sent really good tickets for the first night of one of his operas.

Two days before he died he is reported as saying, 'One must really not keep company with Israelites! Either they are emotionally disturbed about it or it expresses itself in haughtiness'.

One wonderful bit of irony. Wagner's anti-semitism was horribly influential precisely because of his fame, of his genius. It was taken up by Hitler and pronounced holy. It was this, his anti-semitism, that has done most harm to his reputation and most sullied his genius. If he was so wrong about that how can we trust that he was right about anything else?

Wagner had two answers to this difficult Jewish question. One was, not unexpectedly, conversion. Not, however, merely the superficial inconvenience of a religious

73

ceremony but a radical turning around which would have to reach down into the very depths of the Jew's personality. Root and branch. In fact de-Judaization. No longer Jews who are still in their heart of hearts Jewish but true converts who have purged themselves of those 'characteristics which are so difficult to eradicate and are so disadvantageous to our culture'. Something, of course, that can never really be done except in very rare cases, those 'truly sympathetic friends' of the maestro who 'fate has delivered over to me from their tribal allegiance'. Echoes of this attitude much later in the process of de-Nazification which also left one or two inconvenient converts who went through the ceremony only and failed in the root and branch department.

The other answer was even more radical than this. It was 'the violent expulsion of the destructive foreign element'. Violent? Expulsion? Destructive? Cosima mentions in her diaries that four hundred Jews were burned to death in a Viennese synagogue. Wagner's comment, 'Perhaps all Jews should be burned'. Here, then, in an early but quite well rounded form, we have an almost complete Nazi programme in relation to the Jewish question. Its author: Wagner not Nietzsche.

In an extraordinary turn of phrase Wagner told Hermann Levi, the conductor he chose for the great consecration festival that was 'Parsifal', that 'he had to learn how to die'. He meant that he had to replace his Jewish dread of death with the Christian understanding of redemption but the words ring in the ear with quite another meaning.

Then there is Cosima's diary which is vast and, in rather too many ways, not unlike the operas of her second husband. It runs from 1st January 1869, six weeks after moving openly to join Wagner at Tribschen with her two daughters, until 12th February 1883, the evening before his death in Venice. It contains self-importance and anti-semitism on almost every page.

Cosima's diary was written for Siegfried who never read it. A note under the line. Siegfried became a composer in his own right and his opera 'Herzog Wildfang' was heard by Debussy in 1903. Debussy's comment, 'It sounds like a piece of homework by a pupil of Richard Wagner'. Poor Siegfried had an upbringing that sounds horribly like Nietzsche's. His father died when he was fourteen and he was raised by his mother and his four older sisters and half-sisters. A boy surrounded by women. He died only two months after his mother.

Wagner could still have said, and with every justification, that some of his best friends were Jews. He even called them, perhaps even with a little embarrassment, 'our home-grown Israelites'. However, the inflexibility of his theoretical ranting turned into pragmatism in the face of actual, living and breathing Jews. As a race or tribe they may not have been capable as musicians because of the influence of synagogue chanting but when an individual Jewish musician of talent appeared he was welcomed. And these Jews were devoted. Joseph Rubinstein, for a time resident pianist at Wahnfried, made arrangements of Wagner's music and played them to visitors that came to the house. This is the man who was saved from despair about his Jewishness by his association with Wagner's music. When Wagner died he was so distraught that he committed suicide on his grave. The man who set up the vereine to raise money for the festival theatre was Karl Tausig and it was in 1871, at the point when most of Wagner's hopes for the festival theatre were invested in these groups, that he died. He had worked tirelessly for Wagner and the new theatre. Wagner blamed fate for taking from him the 'devoted helpers and interpreters' of his art at the very moment he needed them most. Tausig, of course, was

75

a Jew but Wagner diplomatically ignored this. Cosima confides to her diary that 'he threw himself into Bayreuth with a real frenzy' and that he was 'a great pillar to our enterprise' but she also noted that he 'is dying of typhus! A great shock. Even if he recovers, he is in any case lost to our undertaking; what a lesson to us! To us his death seems to have a metaphysical basis; a poor character, worn out early, one with no real faith, who, however close events brought to us, was always conscious of an alien element (the Jewish)'.

Angelo Neumann, Wagner's best loved singer, was given the parts of both Siegfried and Lohengrin and, as impresario, took the Ring from one end of Europe to the other. Gustav Mahler conducted Wagner in Vienna to great acclaim and Arnold Schoenberg, who heard the performances called them 'beautiful'. Otto Weininger went so far as to call Wagner 'second only to Christ himself'. Wagner thought so much of the critic Heinrich Porges that he attempted to enlist him as his personal secretary. And, as we have seen, Hermann Levi, whose father was a Rabbi, was entrusted with the first performance of Parsifal, a 'Christian-German sacred theatrical play'.

Wagner often needed money and he was shrewd enough to place the 40,000 thalers given to him by Ludwig II with the Jewish banker Hohenemser. He even agreed that the loudest applause at performances of his operas came from the Jews. He said to Cosima that 'Wahnfried seems to be turning into a synagogue'. He wrote of these Jews, 'I simply cannot get rid of them [...] Because of their dealings in paintings, jewellery and furniture, the Jews have an instinct for what is genuine and what can be turned to lasting value'. Wagner's operas?

And in the middle of all this was the 'Bayreuther Blätter', Wagner's own journal, which was sent out to all the vereine and kept his followers in touch with the goings on in Bayreuth. It was designed to praise and justify the operas and the theatre and to this task bent many of Wagner's closest collaborators, some of them his own home-grown Israelites, for example Porges and Rubinstein. Also involved, however, were a clutch of anti-semites who turn-ed its pages into something not a little unpleasant. The editor, Hans von Wolzogen, ended up actively involved in the anti-semitic movement. Just another muddle and paradox from the group around the maestro.

And how does Nietzsche sum up this substitute father? How does he describe Wagner's music? Answer - as a sickness which stands over against the other, the clean, the healthy, the easy masterpiece. Which is? Carmen, 'This music approaches lightly, with subtlety and politeness. It moves on tender feet, straightforward, honest and above all healthy. No masks, no lying, no sickness. What is good is light. This is not the music of the north, of a damp climate, but of the south, of Africa. It has a southern, brown, burnt sensibility. It is vital to Mediterraneanise music'.

All this against the lie of the grand style. The Wagnerian insistence. The constant repetition until one is driv-en to believe. The maestro raps his knuckle on the table and calls us to attention. Listen to this! he exhorts us. This is great music, important music. It contains the steam of the Wagnerian ideal. Driven on by pressure, Wagner imposes upon us. With that strange and slightly unconvincing smile on his face he holds out to us something in his hand. It is a magnifying glass. We take hold of it and instantly, as our fingers close upon its handle, we lose all trust in our own eyes, placing this glass in front of our faces, we see everything distorted and enlarged including Wagner himself. We see Wagner's image of life magnified, magnificent, impressed upon us with every possible device which his enormous artistry could contrive and we lose ourselves in his vision of another world.

We lose ourselves and drown. This is Wagner's gift and it is the gift of death. His art induces breathlessness and sweating. The heat in the auditorium becomes more and more stifling. There is a slight smell of incense in the air and we feel as if some sickness has taken over, a sickness which we almost welcome, which we have brought upon ourselves through the medium of Wagner. 'Is Wagner a human being at all? Is he not rather an illness? He makes everything he touches ill - he has even made music ill. I feel the strongest urge to open all the windows. Air, more air! But we have no energy to open the windows. We don't even want to breathe any more. It is a sign of our exhaustion that we stay in our seats and marvel'. Sometimes the sick are attracted by what harms them. Wagner increases sickness and that is why he is attractive to those who want to be sick, who want to put their lives into the hands of this anti-doctor who holds out in his hand a drug which is almost as much a poison as a cure, the same drug that, given in large enough quantities and in the right circumstances, can all too easily kill. His art is an appeal to inartistic people; all means are welcome which may help towards bearing the right fruit, ripe and ready to fall. It is calculated not to produce an artistic effect but an effect upon the nerves in general. Wagner excites the world-weary and weather-beaten who seek shelter and want to be easily convinced. To this end he has corrupted music and the drama. Exciting the nerves of the weary he also, at the very same stroke of the pen, convinces them of the significance of their tiredness, that only as exhausted and dead to the world can they appreciate what they hear and exalt in the fact - in the music that makes them want to be weary and the weariness they need to exalt in the music. Wagner gives us a heavy-hearted and drowsy happiness.

The secret of the magniloquent rantings at Nuremberg is the secret of the music of Wagner. They are one and the same. Exalt in the fact that you cannot help but exalt. What is needed is not beauty, not seriousness nor thinking. Why have beauty? Why not choose instead what is great, sublime, larger than life, gigantic - that which moves masses. After all it is easier to be gigantic than to be beautiful and easier, much much easier, to be persuaded than to think. Thinking, after all, is critical and demands, as well as listening, a certain resistance to what is heard. And who persuades the easily persuaded? Who convinces the throng who already believe what they have not yet heard? Only the tyrant whose skill is in hypnosis rather than beauty or thought. Wagner was not born a musician but became one because the tyrant within him, his actor's genius, compelled him to it. His music has no law or style, no melody or counterpoint but is only theatrical rhetoric. One has to act to achieve great success with the public. Only the actor, the deceiver, can arouse great enthusiasms.

Although expressed with great subtlety, this is not new in the writing of Nietzsche. The great philosophers of the ancient world knew all about the relation of art to spectacle, of the seeking after applause and the admiration of the masses. Nietzsche studied and wrote about Plato and Aristotle whilst Hitler never gave them a moment's thought. Plato died writing the Laws while watching the Greek world fall apart. Listen to Plato at the consummation of his life, setting down laws for the Athenians, 'There arose leaders of unmusical illegality, poets who were ignorant of the just and the lawful in music and, because they were unduly possessed by a spirit of pleasure, mixed up all the different kinds of music together and by so doing unknowingly bore false witness against music as a thing without any standards of correctness. The only way of judging the quality of this music is in the pleasure which it gives the audience and thus the audience came to think they were qualified to pass judgement on it. In the place of a genuine aristocracy of music there sprang forth a kind of theatrocracy, a rule of the theatre'. And here is the lesson for the Wagnerians which they fearlessly repeated; thinking that they knew, men became fearless and this fearlessness soon became effrontery. Aristotle followed Plato and also knew the dangers of displacing art with spectacle. He wrote his 'Poetics' as Alexander, the master of the Greek world, was marching his armies eastward in another massive and short lived conquest echoed by Napoleon and ... Aristotle understood the relation between a people's art and a people's army. He knew that spectacle, though an attraction, is the least artistic of all the parts of tragedy and has the least (and I repeat the ancient master so as not to lose his point) has the least to do with the art of poetry. The tragic effect is possible without being put on a stage in front of the public for performance by actors. This, the spectacle, is more a matter for the costumier than for the poet or artist. The great man does not retreat from his greatness and displace it into his art, only the little man does that, 'the Mozarts and the Haydns, the classics. These are the little men who are little because all their greatness is in their music, their greatness has gone out of them and into their art. 'These are the anonymous men of art who move with light feet, with wit, with grace, with great logic, who dance with the stars, with exuberant spirits, who know the southern trembling of light and the smooth sea, who have, in a word, perfection'. Wagner is not like this. He is much more important. He knows that he is much more important. He has weight. With Wagner the greatness is never displaced. Wagner marches onward, like Christian soldiers, with drums and flutes at the head of all the artists of delivery, of presentation, of virtuosity.

Nietzsche wrote, 'I recall that in 1870, during a study of ancient rhythmic patterns, I was seeking five and seven measure phrases and counted my way through Meistersinger and Tristan. In the process I discovered something about Wagner's own rhythmic processes. He has such an aversion to anything mathematical, anything rigidly symmetrical [...] that he tends to extend four beat phrases into five beats, six beat phrases into seven [...] At times, even though this may be sacrilegious, I'm reminded of the style of Bernini, who can no longer bear to have even his pillars plain, but has to animate them from top to bottom with scrollwork'. This is an art full of over-excitement and glorified extravagance. Again, 'Among the dangerous after-effects of Wagner, the will-to-animate-at-any-cost strikes me as one of the worst, because quick as a flash it becomes affectation, or cunning'.

More, 'Wagner's music is simply bad music, perhaps the worst ever created. When a musician can no longer count up to three he becomes dramatic, he becomes Wagnerian'. Not style, not counterpoint, not the substance or thought of music but merely the effects that music can be used to produce. To produce effects rather than beauty, to use music rather than to make music, that is the genius of Wagner, the genius of the tyrant. Beauty refuses to acknowledge its audience. It happens in spite of its audience. It faces in another direction altogether. At its core is a fatal refusal to convince, to produce effects. At its core is mystery. But Wagner knows his audience and writes for it, 'Who equals the persuasive power of his gestures? Who else starts with gestures and then fits the music to them? What is his working method? He begins with the third scene in order to prove his work to himself by the strength of its ultimate effect and then builds around this a series of powerful scenes each one stronger than the other and then, between these, he puts a lot of crafty stupidity because it doesn't matter what is in between. It will ride on the strength of what has gone before and what will certainly come in the next moment'. The only greatness of Wagner's music is in their subservience to gesture and to the effect which gesture hopes to achieve. And is this not tyrannical?

Nietzsche describes Wagner's audience and it is Hitler's audience also, 'The best among those who sit there - German youths, horned Siegfrieds and other Wagnerians - need the sublime, the profound, the overwhelming. And the others who sit there also - the culture morons, the petty snobs, those who thank the Lord that they have an easy digestion, in a word, the people. Those need the sublime, the profound, the overwhelming. Why is this so? Listen to the thoughtless reasoning of the people, of the mass, of those who lose their individuality in a crowd. This is what they say, "Who can throw us must be strong, who can elevate us must be divine and who can help us to have intimations must be divine"'. Not thought but something else, the expectation of thought, the hope of thought, the myriad of unborn thoughts that wait to spring up like magic in the mind. The willingness to be given a thought. The longing to be persuaded.

Wagner had learnt this lesson and decided to throw them, to elevate them and to give them intimations. This may not be easy, not everyone can do it, but it is far from impossible, almost as far from impossible as the creation of beauty which is itself impossible. Beauty only creates itself or always fails to create itself but thoughts can be inserted into the mind that is ready for them, that has suspended its ability to criticise, that is willing to be hypnotised. Wagner is like Hitler in this, that he is a master of hypnotic tricks and Nietzsche understood this perfectly. Listen to him again, 'People are thrown by passion and brute strength but not by subtlety. Beware counterpoint. Beware melody. Beware beauty because it is difficult. Passion is ugly. The easy thought is like a sledgehammer. It effects the brain instantly and is irrefutable. I cannot like music that has no ambition other than to hypnotise the nerves'. Again, 'People are elevated by ideals so let us have plenty of ideals. Let us walk on clouds and create a mythology of gods and demons'. Let us mythologise the Nordic and demonise the Jews, the gypsies, the disabled. Let us harangue the infinite and surround ourselves with symbols. The Germans hear great symbols approach from out of foggy distances and resound in his music with muted thunder. Is it any wonder that Hitler loved Wagner and Wagner's music? Is it any wonder that Wagner hated the Jews? No wonder. No wonder.

Wagner is at heart, just as Hitler was at heart, a little bourgeois. And this is why each knew so well how telling their effects would be. 'Wagner's plots are all bourgeois plots. Retell his tales without their mythological proportions and they lose almost all of their power. Imagine Parsifal as a candidate for a degree in theology who entered college with a secondary school education. Stripped of their heroic skin Wagner's plots are almost indistinguishable from Madame Bovary. Turn this around and you could imagine Flaubert making his heroines into Scandinavian or Carthaginian gods and offering them fully formed to Wagner for his next libretto'.

But this is more than a little unfair to Flaubert whose style is not at odds with his content. Wagner's effect is deep, profound, strong, dangerous and with little relation to the little people it has turned into gods for the purpose. But his audience was not fooled. They knew he was telling them that they were godlike, that in the mass they could be clothed as gods and do great things. Onward Nordic soldiers. Actions not thoughts. With Wagner began the age of the Teuton. The arrival of Wagner on the stage of art coincides with the arrival of the Reich on the stage of politics, 'Both of these are Teutonic - definition of the Teuton - obedience and long legs! Wagner commands and never has obedience been deeper'.

A call to action which leaves mere words behind. Not a call to thought which delves ever deeper into words. Rhetoric not dialectic. That is the great Wagnerian secret. Not mere music. Not music for music's sake. A rose is not a rose but has its uses. Wagner repeated one basic proposition all his life long, 'that his music was not merely music but much, much more, even infinitely more'. That music reached way beyond itself into the world of action. The music was subservient to this aim and has to conform to it. Music was a means to an end. A mere means. No musician, no real musician, would talk like that.

After grumbling about Wagner, Brahms was asked to admit that his music had its glorious moments and Brahms reply was, 'Yes, and its bloody boring quarters of an hour'. Mozart, looking down from his box in the magic theatre created by Hesse saw Brahms and Wagner, in their day the most extreme contrasts possible, each followed by thousands of men in black who represented the players of all those notes which according to divine judgement were superfluous and he told Steppenwolf who was in the box beside him that, 'until they have paid the debt of their time it cannot be known whether anything personal to themselves is left over to stand to their credit so they can gain redemption'.

And Nietzsche summed it up, 'How shall we satisfy our thirst for wholesale homage! Could one not select from the composer's music some hundred bars of good music which appeal to the heart because they have heart: could one not go aside with this little theft and forget all the rest!'

The end of this relationship between the composer who thought and the thinker who composed is shrouded in mystery.

Nietzsche spent the winter of 1876-7 in Sorrento with Rée and another young man called Brenner in the house of Melwida von Meysenbug. It just so happened that the Wagners came on holiday there for a month from October 5th, escaping to the sun like Nietzsche, and had booked into the Hotel Victoria which was almost next door to Malwida's residence, the Villa Rubinacci. These four were often invited to spend time with the Wagners. Nietzsche's tense cheeriness was noticed but as he had said nothing of his change of opinion about Wagner and he never objected to spending time at their hotel, nothing was said openly.

One day the two went for a walk. They strolled up along the coast to the top of the hill where there was a magnificent view over the sea with its islands and inlets. It was a lovely autumn day and Wagner said that it made him feel in 'a mood of departure'. He began to speak about 'Parsifal' but instead of telling Nietzsche about the opera he went into a long and complex description of a profound Christian mystical experience which he had recently had. The confirmed atheist now announced earnest sympathies with Christianity and spoke of his deep love of Holy Communion. Had he really dared to announce this to Nietzsche of all people? Was this a real conversion or merely an attempt to cuddle up to the preconceptions of his audience? After all, he had said that 'the Germans have no interest in heathen gods and heroes. They want to see something Christian'. Nietzsche's response to all of this? A strained silence. He excused himself and left Wagner standing there under the darkening evening sky. They never met again.

This fantastical tale emanates, as you might expect, from the pen of Elizabeth who was keen to cover up all disagreements between the two men. In fact, Nietzsche would hardly have been surprised by Wagner's conversion to Christianity which had clearly been on the cards for ages. Neither would he have been shocked by 'Parsifal', the libretto of which had been read to him during the Christmas of 1869, a good seven years earlier. Cosima records in her diaries that Nietzsche listened in complete silence and that it left 'a deep impression'.

The real reason for the break might have been somewhat different. In October 1877 Wagner wrote that letter to Otto Eiser, Nietzsche's doctor, suggesting that his patient's illness was the result of too much masturbation and that he should persuade him to go and take the waters. Nietzsche was furious at this and calls it 'a vicious and destructive coarseness on the composer's part'. Wagner had caused him 'mortal offence'.

However, Nietzsche's reaction to 'Parsifal' is well known. In it 'everything is too Christian. No flesh and too much blood (the communion in particular gets too full-bloodied)'. He said nothing about his reaction to the composer. Nietzsche's reaction was not wrong. Cosima once made a public comparison between 'Parsifal' and the Gospel to which Wagner is said to have nodded in agreement. Hitler, of course, saw 'Parsifal' as 'a glorification of our pure Aryan blood'. The critic Hartmut Zerlinsky, writing in 1982, suggested, in agreement with Hitler, that 'Parsifal' is a piece of anti-semitic pro-Aryan propaganda finding in the word 'redemption (erlösung) the word 'final solution' (endlösung') and suggesting that the piece should never be performed, a suggestion which has been taken seriously in Israel.

After Wagner's death Nietzsche wrote, 'It is hard to be for six years the enemy of the man one most honours'.

Another aside. Wagner's music makes people mad. Ludwig Schnorr died soon after his appearance as the first Tristan and Wagner understood that the opera had been the cause. Anders went insane working on the same part and Scaria died mad after performing 'Parsifal'. Marie Wilt, learned the part of Brünnhilde in three weeks and admitted days before her suicide, 'That finished me'. Wagner wrote to Mathilde Wesendonck, 'This Tristan is turning into something frightful! [...] Only mediocre performances can save me. Completely good ones are bound to make people mad'.

Wagner's was a death in Venice. He went there in 1882 and stayed in the Palazzo Vendramin, taking over the eighteen rooms on the first floor. As usual he had a study draped in silks and satins and heavily scented. Here he read his last Nietzsche book, 'The Gay Science'. Neither the book nor the change of scenery could help and the chest cramps he had experienced earlier got worse. He was dosed with opium. Joukovsky, who was living with them, found Wagner playing the piano and sketched his head. The drawing is on graph paper and the master is smiling and his eyes are half closed as if playing from memory.

On February 13th he pulled urgently on the bell rope calling for the doctor and his wife. He died of a heart attack in Cosima's arms. He was writing an essay for the 'Bayreuther Blätter' and the page lay open on his desk. The last word on the paper was 'Tragik'. Before nightfall a shocked and respectful world received the news of his death.

A curious incident took place at his funeral. The Munich Wagner Association, the first of many of these associations soon to spring up, brought a wreath to place on the grave. On it they had put an inscription. It read, 'Redemption for the redeemer'. This inscription immediately became famous. Everyone was lost in admiration for the lofty principles which had inspired it. But perhaps, one should be allowed to make just one small correction to this inscription. Not 'redemption for the redeemer' but rather 'redemption from the redeemer'.

Who is the art lover after Wagner? Who is the archetypal Wagner disciple? What did Wagner breed and multiply? Above all else the presumption of the layman, of the art-idiot, of the kind that organises art associations and visits to the opera and who knows how to judge art because he understands instinctively what his fellow art-lover is going to think, because he has been persuaded and even cudgelled by the very music he imagines he is then free to criticise. A falling back on the notions of genius as an excuse for such ignorance, not

87

genius that overcomes rules but as an excuse for the failure of skill. The rise of the layman means the fall of the real artist, of conscientious training in the forms of art, of the nobility of real sweat, of the careful learning of rules before breaking them. Writing without any attention to the rules is not a breaking of rules but a careful tiptoeing around them, an ignorance of them. This layman is already persuaded before he walks reverently through the ornate portals of the concert hall with other believers who take their seats around him half terrified by the experience they are merely repeating, 'To put this plainly, belief in dilettantism'. Or to put this even more plainly, Hitler's paintings.

And doesn't the famous marching song of the SA, the Horst Wessel Lied sound as if it might have been composed by Richard Wagner?

Nietzsche, the failed musician, understood Wagner, the failed actor. Both of them were co-opted as stars of the Third Reich by Adolf Hitler, the failed painter and architect.

Before so much else, a crisis for Elizabeth in which she almost went under but finally overcame, a crisis which put her on her learning curve and which was a kind of dress rehearsal for so many later successes. A crisis that appeared in the form of Lou von Salomé. The occasion, the first performance of Parsifal. The place, Bayreuth. The year, 1882, the 'Parsifal Year' and the year of Wagner's death. Under the full weight of Wagner worship the two women who were pulling Nietzsche's soul in different directions met and the battle of the old world with the new took place in miniature. Elizabeth, the representative of petty bourgeois, small town, Naumberg conventionality against the free and feminist, the never in love against the always in love, the self-possessed against the intense, the dying against the almost born.

The core of that hatred that never died was the love that never died. Memories of Santo Giulio, the island in the lake called Monte Sacro in memory of Saint Francis of Assisi, memories of that moment among the hills that rose out of the lake. Here went Nietzsche with Lou von Salomé, the two irreverent atheists walking among the sacred ruins in the hearing of bells from a monastery which was a living ornament to the church they questioned. They trod the paths up the hillside. What happened on that walk is still a mystery. They spent too long on the island offending both Rée and Lou's mother who they had left behind. According to Lou, they stayed to see the sunset on Santa Rosa but the sunset at Santa Rosa cannot be seen from the top of the island so it was not a sunset that held them back but something else. The closest Nietzsche ever got to a kiss? Or more? Enough to create a memory that stayed with him to the end of his life. Many years later Lou had not forgotten and told Ernst Pfeiffer, 'I do not know whether I kissed Nietzsche on Monte Sacro or not'. And Nietzsche also never forgot, 'To you I owe the most beautiful dream of my life'.

They had indeed been '6000 feet above man and time' but returned to sea level, to a world three hundred feet below those hazy memories and to the certainty of witnesses who knew that they had tarried much too long. When Elizabeth got to learn of this she saw instantly that her closeness to her brother was at risk. She waited for she was nothing if not patient and was learning how to choose the moment.

Later a visit to Wagner's empty house at Tribschen where Lou had to listen to the history of Nietzsche's friendship with the maestro. She wrote in her book on Nietzsche, 'For a long, long time he sat in silence on the shore of the

89

lake profoundly engrossed in intense memories. Then, while drawing in the wet sand with his cane, he softly spoke of those past times. And when he looked up there were tears in his eyes'. Another dream which was fading, another love which stayed with him to the end of his life. He told her of happy memories that had ripened and faded. Did this earlier suffering prolong his suffering now? She agreed to spend time with him and his family in Tautenberg where Elizabeth had planned 'an idyllic nest' for the summer which had not included Lou. But first to Bayreuth.

Elizabeth came with Förster and Lou with Nietzsche. At first no disaster was anticipated, Lou writing to Nietzsche that 'Elizabeth is almost my sister too', but it was not long before the prim sister was being scandalised by Lou's behaviour. She was involved in a series of horrors, allowing Joukovsky to design costumes for the opera on her lithe and almost naked body, strolling unaccompanied with men through public places and even attending a séance with no other women in the room. In Tautenberg Elizabeth exaggerated the snippets of rude conversation that she overheard and even noticed that Lou didn't wash her underwear as often as she might and left her room untidy. In Tautenberg, however, Lou and Nietzsche got on famously, walking among the pine trees and talking endlessly. There was 'a meeting of like thoughts, like feelings and ideas', an openness that Elizabeth recognised as the worst kind of danger signal where her brother was concerned. There was even some talk of setting up home with Rée. She now became determined to split the two apart. Later she would deal with her brother but first she attacked this new follower of his. But she was still learning and not quite ready to show the kind of control she was later to learn so well.

When she and Lou returned together to Jena on their way to Tautenberg she began her campaign. She tried first with advice about morals. Taking Lou aside as if she were her 'younger sister' she told her that a girl's most precious possession was her honour, something which was easily lost. She told her that a girl had to be so very careful and that a careless glance, a rash word and it would be lost for ever. How shocked she must have been when Lou could control herself no longer and burst out laughing. Elizabeth was hurt, but not so much as she was at Lou's response to her next line of attack. Didn't she know that her association with her brother was hurting his reputation. Had she simply failed to appreciate how very important a person he was? Did she not realise that, because she was associated with Nietzsche, her lewd behaviour was affecting his reputation with the Wagner circle. Lou was surprised by this as she had no idea that Nietzsche had any reputation either on his own account or with the Wagner circle and told Elizabeth that he was no longer spoken of among them, that as far as they were concerned, he was dead. This was more painful to Elizabeth than anything. She went pale and stuttered out that she would do anything to halt the arrangement that they had been planning for a ménage à trois with Rée, that such a thing might be acceptable among Russians but here among civilised people it was quite out of the question.

Lou exploded, 'Don't get the idea that I am interested in your brother, or am in love with him. I could spend the whole night in one room with him without getting in the least bit aroused. It was your brother who first spoiled our study plan with the lowest intentions. He was the one who started to talk about friendship when he realised that he could not have me for anything else. It was your brother and not I who was the first to suggest "free love"'.

Elizabeth had no way of responding to this other than to collapse in tears. Her face horribly pale, she rushed for the bathroom, her hand over her mouth but, before she could reach it, she vomited, all her spleen coming out through her hands and onto the polished parquet flooring.

After this Elizabeth got to work spitting out venom in every way she could. Letters went out from her every which way. She wrote that Lou was a Finnish Jewess and worse, an ugly Jewess. She got under her brother's skin

DAVID POLLARD

91

and co-opted him as an ally in her strategy. She always knew how to twist his emotions to her own advantage. She told him that Lou had been cavorting with his Wagnerian enemies at Bayreuth, exactly the thing to destroy Nietzsche's confidence. He heard her out with a white face and retired already half defeated. She insisted that Lou was a women who only wanted to suck up to the rich and famous and, as soon as she discovered that Nietzsche was neither of these, had backed off. It didn't take much more of his sister's nagging before he was calling Lou 'a dry, dirty, bad smelling monkey with false breasts'. Nietzsche's words or Elizabeth's? She soon convinced the poor man that Lou had left him for Rée and that it was Rée who had poisoned her against him. A logical thing to think as it was partly true, 'It is he who speaks of me as a low character and common egotist, who desires to use everything only for his own ends [...] who reproaches me with having [...] pursued the filthiest of designs on Fraülein Salomé'. Rée is a 'liar and sneaking slanderer to the core'. He and Lou 'are not worthy to lick the soles of my boots'. Again, 'She unites in herself all the human qualities that are to me the most revolting and repulsive'.

But it didn't take him long to realise where the venom was coming from. He spoke of his sister's 'revenge on Fraulein Salomé' writing, 'My sister has become Lou's deadly enemy [...] I have against me the Naumberg virtue [...] I have become the victim of a merciless revengefulness'. Her life of Nietzsche, written in 1904 called the relationship between her brother and Lou Salomé a lamentable error and claimed that Nietzsche could never stand women of Lou's type, a type that loved only enjoyment and creature comforts. A year later she repeated much of this in an article in 'Die Zukunft', commenting that Lou's book on her brother was nothing more than a feeble effort to regain the love of Rée. In the first volume of her biography she went over the whole thing again adding a few more lies for good measure such as Lou's supposed childhood affair with the priest Hendrick Gillot in St Petersburg. All the recriminations were repeated in 1935 in her

'Nietzsche and Women'. Lou, in her dignified way, refused to rise to these scurrilous baits and answered all this malice with silence. Years later Freud wrote, 'I am very pleased to hear that you are working on your memoirs. It has often annoyed me to find your relationship with Nietzsche mentioned in a way which was obviously hostile to you and which could not possibly correspond to the facts. You have put up with everything and have been far too decent'. Even here in her summing up of that relationship she never says a word of Elizabeth's slanders. Nietzsche later wrote of this incident as 'the toughest I have ever had to chew' and always blamed Elizabeth for destroying the one love of his life, 'It is painful for me to hear my sister's voice [...] I am the victim of her merciless desire for vengeance'. For a long time he stopped speaking to her. Ironic that Salomé means 'peace'.

As for Nietzsche, after Lou his life was a posthumous existence of recriminations mixed with impossible hopes, 'If I should take my own life, there would not be much cause for mourning. What do you care about my fantasies? - You did not even care for my truth. I want you to consider that I am, after all, nothing but a semi-lunatic, tortured by headaches, who has been completely unhinged by his long solitude. You have done harm, you have caused injury [...] If I had created you I would have given you [...] a little more love for me [...] Remember this cattishness of yours that is not capable of love [...] Farewell my dear Lou. I shall not see you again'. And yet, in his life of Salomé, Peters writes, 'Try as he might he could not forget Lou [...] She had shamefully deceived him. Frustrated in his efforts to hurt [her...] Nietzsche's disappointed love turned against himself. He talked of suicide. He called himself a madman and boasted of taking overdoses of opium'. Later Nietzsche wrote 'You have caused much damage. You have done harm not only me but all the people who have

93

loved me. This sword hangs over you'. He even told her that one of her breasts was false and years later, after an operation for cancer in which she had had a breast removed, she was forced to fill her blouse with padding and commented 'Nietzsche was right. Now I do have a false breast'.

A note should, perhaps, be added to these memories. Lou wrote years later comparing Nietzsche and Rée as philosophers that 'of the two [...Rée's] was the more acute mind' and even Nietzsche wrote to Lou, 'I always admire how well armed your arguments are from the point of view of logic. This is in fact something of which I am incapable'.

And then there is Nietzsche's, 'I thought they had sent me an angel [...] but she was no angel'.

Overbeck wrote, 'I have the impression of a light that flickers and am prepared for the worst'. But he didn't understand the Nietzschian heart. Nietzsche's next book begins, 'When Zarathustra was thirty years old he left his home and the lake of his home and went into the mountains. Here he had the companionship of his spirit [...] but at last his heart turned [...] I must descend into the depths [...] I must go down'. He commands, 'Flee into solitude. You   live too close to the trivial and the spiteful. Flee from their invisible revenge'. 'Forget that happy hour [...] Alas, to where has that happy hour now fled [..] To where did my tender longing flee?' Nietzsche wrote 'Thus Spake Zarathustra', twisting free from the fate he had been handed. 'He who cannot obey himself will be commanded. Man is   something that must be overcome'. This is the first of his posthumous books which are riddled with the motif of the man who can overcome himself.

Elizabeth also never forgot an injury. The feud, in a quite different way, continued until her death. She was not exactly a forgiving woman and certainly persistent in pursuit of her aims. As soon as she heard of Lou's break with her brother and that she was living in Berlin with Rée, she saw her way. After all, a criminal act is a criminal act and a useful threat should not be cast aside. She wrote to both the families of the offending couple, threatening prosecution and demanding that Lou should be hustled back home. She made the letters public and caused a sensation which nearly overwhelmed her brother who even threat-ened to fight a duel with Rée and suffered mental agonies in his retreat. But Elizabeth, as always, forgot the side show when the main battle was being fought.

Lou, however, was equal to Elizabeth and stood her ground. She did not return to Russia. Neither did she give up Rée even when she found herself outlawed by everyone. In fact she gave Rée the kind of life that she had given Nietzsche. Their platonic relationship in Berlin was for him 'a pseudo life'. He would roam the streets at night to avoid her sexual presence back in their little apartment and came to be known as her 'maid-of-honour', a fact which she relayed apparently quite innocent of the implicit criticism of his masculinity. He was quite happy to tag along behind her and she was quite happy to let him. She was her own woman and would not be ruled by anyone, least of all by Elizabeth Nietzsche.

Unsurprisingly, Elizabeth later denied any meddling, 'my brother had broken off the relationship of his own accord without any outside influence' and anyway he had always considered the idea of the three of them living together as 'an offence against the proprieties'. She maintained that neither Rée nor Nietzsche ever had the slightest desire to marry her. The difficult question of Rée's early suicide, the death of the man of 'grey-haired philosophy, of the rationalist', is not mentioned. He had always carried a small phial of poison in his jacket pocket but, in the event, he jumped off a cliff into the River Inn which winds its way through the Engadine where he had often walked with Nietzsche. His body was found by a workman in the early morning of 29th October 1901. Thus are the sensibilities of the bourgeois off-loaded onto others who had little thought of them. For Elizabeth, Lou's refusal to marry either Rée or her brother was merely because she 'was looking forward to a far more brilliant match'.

And if Lou had not run off with Rée. If she and Nietzsche had married and there had been no posthumous existence? What kind of creative life would Nietzsche have followed? With such a wife and such a disciple he would hardly have had that particular posthumous existence and later, not so very much later, maybe no other posthumous existence of clinics and controls. Who knows? As it is, a new life opened with the first pages of Zarathustra.

PART II

Paraguay

The Försters were not the first white people with strong ideals and a foolhardy disregard for danger to make their way to the Americas in search of utopia, or rather, of Eldorado, a land of promise rather than a promised land. The first to sight the continent was Bjarni Herjolfsson who was blown there by mistake and refused to land. He returned to Norway and sold his boat to Leif Ericson who repeated the trip and did land. He found the place wonderful, 'The land was so fertile that it was unnecessary to store cattle fodder for the winter, for there was no frost and the grass did not wither much'. They even found grapes and named the place Vineland. History forgot them and the continent was not called Leifland. Nor was it called Columboland after the next visitor who landed, sent by those very combined monarchs who expelled the Jews from Spain in the annus mirabilis of 1492. He refused to accept that the place existed and went on trying to find a way round it, probed this way and that, refusing to see the evidence in front of his eyes, that is, that Columboland was not Cathay.

Ericson went to the North, Columbus went to the middle but it was Amerigo Vespucci who went to the South and it was Vespucci who really saw the place for the first time and wrote vividly of a New World. He had been given his education by an uncle and had joined the Medici family bank and worked for them in Seville where one of his tasks was to assist Gianoto Berardi in fitting out the ships which voyaged westward. Vespucci succeeded Berardi and then succeeded Columbus. His affairs got into a mess and he accepted an invitation to captain one of the free voyages to the Indies. He sailed across the ocean, then south off the coast of Brazil and, following the coastline, entered a huge estuary which was later called the River of Silver.

Following the voyagers came the settlers, a string of other conquerors who, fired by stories of immense wealth and by their own brand of religious zeal, stuck little pins topped with European flags all over the map of the continent. This is the eternal story of colonisation, the search for Camelot. Interestingly, there are camelotes in Paraguay. They are little islands which the flood of the great river tugs away from the banks and forces downstream where they finally come to rest in a quite inappropriate environment. Tigers and snakes come ashore in Monte Video or in Buenos Aires and terrify the inhabitants who are unexpectedly scratched or bitten. Perhaps the moral is to stay put. The Försters made the same mistake and landed up where they had no right to be.

Spain's greatest pilot was Juan Díaz de Solis. He came to the New World in 1508 with Vicente Yañez Pinzón. They sailed on past the mouth of the River of Silver without even noticing that it was there. Five years later King Ferdinand provided de Solis with three frigates and on this voyage the estuary was located and named Rio de Solis. He sailed up the river and mapped it, sending out a longboat to poke about along its shoreline. The savages persuaded him ashore and he followed them into a clearing in the forest where they cut him down and ate him. The expedition, now leaderless, returned to Spain leaving one of the frigates stranded near the island of Santa Catherina. The eighteen survivors found refuge on the island and learned Guariní, the local language, during their enforced stay there. One of this group was Aleixo Garcia, a Portuguese adventurer, who was the first white man to make his way up the Rio Paraguay.

Aleixo left Santa Catherina for home with only three or four followers but was later sent by Charles I with four ships and six hundred men to follow the route of Magellan and find the riches of the Orient. They moved westwards, found the falls of Iguassú, crossed the River Paraná and entered Paraguay. They made an alliance with the native Guaranís and travelled on, following the golden setting sun to the gold of the Incas. The White King, Huana Cápac, fought off the army with great vigour and they had to give up their hopes of territory and make do with the silver which was plentiful and which they looted. On the return journey they were murdered by the Guaranís. Garcia had been the first white man to see the great falls, the first to enter Paraguay, the first to make an alliance with the Guaraní, the first to cross the centre of the continent and the first to ford the Chaco and see any part of the great empire of the Incas. He was also the first to die because of the silver. The first but not the last.

News of the silver reached the east coast and the ears of another adventurer, Sebastian Cabot. He sailed up the rivers as far as Peru and, on his return found the natives who had murdered Garcia carrying his silver. He it was who named the river Rio de la Plata. Charles V eventually laid claim to the entire area to stop it falling into the hands of the Portuguese and appointed one Martínez de Irala, as governor. Irala set up his capital in Asunción. Ideal. Paraguay was located at the head of the great river system that flowed down to the coast from the Andes, the mountain chain which was made entirely of silver. Simply dig up the mountains and carry them back to the Holy Roman Emperor. Irala, unlike later settlers, didn't let notions of racial purity worry him too much. In his last will and testament he writes, 'I say and declare and confess that I have and God has given me in this province certain daughters and sons, who are; Diego Martínez de Irala and Antonio de Irala and Doña Ginebra de Irala, children of myself and Maria my servant; and Doña Isabel de Irala, daughter of Agueda my servant; and Doña Ursula de Irala, daughter of Leonora my servant; and Martín Pérez de Irala, son of Scolastica my servant and ...' In this way were the peoples mixed and Irala got the title of 'Father of the Nation'.

The Jesuits came in on the coat-tails of the conquistadores. The first Bishop struggled into Asunción in 1556 and in 1588 three Jesuits arrived with the express purpose of converting the Guaraní. They did this, of course, by setting them to work. Their produce (Yerba Mate, cotton, tobacco, hides and wood) was sold abroad to great profit for the Church. Soon enough the lay conquerors wanted a cut of all this cheap labour and eventually managed to kick the Jesuits out of the country and grab it for themselves. Thus did colonisation take its course.

But Paraguay was lucky. The Jesuits had been forced to leave by decree before the middle of the eighteenth century and the route across the Chaco to the silver mines had proved too difficult. The Guaraní were untrainable and relapsed into their natural indolence and their own religion. Buenos Aires took over from Asunción and the place returned to its natural state. A return to Eden rather than an advance to the millennium. Even today Paraguay is the only country in South America which is bilingual and has a literature in its own original language. A German wrote, 'The community which comprised the early white population of Paraguay was essentially of a daredevil order, otherwise it would never have penetrated to that remote spot'. This is just as true of the New Germans as is was of the old Spaniards. Its isolation also made it easier for dictators to rule there well into the second half of the twentieth century.

The story of dictators runs naturally on from the story of voyagers and colonisers, all of them searching for Camelots of one kind or another. This new story starts with Dr José Gaspar Rodriguez de Francia who was first to make himself dictator for life and held the title of El Supremo. He was glorified by Carlyle along with other heroes of the continent. These were Bolivar, 'the Washington of Columbia', Iturbide, 'the Napoleon of Mexico' and General San Martin, whose portrait Carlyle had seen 'hung between those of Napoleon and the Duke of Wellington'. This 'lean iron Francia' is a 'remarkable human individual'. At Francia's funeral, Reverend Manuel Pérez took as his text, 'The Lord raised up a Saviour for the children of Israel, who delivered them'.

Next came the father and son team of Carlos Antonio and Francisco Solano López. López Père quickly made himself the biggest landowner in the area and saw that helping the country grow rich would help him grow rich. He is thus called enlightened. His son took up the succession but was not so enlightened. His military engineer, George Thompson, described him as 'a monster without parallel' who 'is short but has a commanding presence [...] is fond of military finery, especially in his staff, and has a somewhat peculiar strut when walking'. He was quickly brought down by initiating a war against all of his powerful neighbours at the same time, a war on three fronts. Ignacio González eulogised him as follows, 'A whole Race (sic) was incarnate in him, a youthful, artistic and courageous Race, who knew how to snatch from the claws of death the secret of Immortality'.

Lopez was followed in his turn by half a century of chaos - thirty-two presidents and one triumvirate. This chaos was broken by the coup led by Colonel Rafael Franco in 1936. Just as another Franco, Francisco, was leading his own coup back in Europe. The key document of his rule is Decree number 152 which in part states that his regime 'is of the same character as the totalitarian transformations occurring in contemporary Europe'. He was followed, after two

101

further coups d'état, by General Estigarronoa who put all power into the hands of the executive which he headed in order to be able to 'deal at a moment's notice with social and economic problems'. Power was legalised in the hands of the president for the first time. Constitutionally, parliament 'would collaborate in matters concerned with legislation' and the executive would 'act within the law'. But, Well! After arranging for absolute power under the constitution Estigarronoa died in a plane crash and the cabinet chose General Higinio Morinigo to succeed him. He immediately took advantage of his predecessor's good work, crushed the usual series of coups d'état against him and surprised everyone by making himself supremo. Of course, he allied himself with the pro-axis powers who were established in Buenos Aires and encouraged German firms, propagandists and spies to do what they liked in the country. He survived by declaring war on the axis powers in plenty of time to be of real help to the allies, that is, in February 1945. Eventually Morinigo was forced out of the country but was soon followed by another general, this time called Alfredo Stroessner, a happy mixture of Spanish and German. He kept going for half a century more.

This story of conquerors and supremos in Paraguay fitted more or less uncomfortably with another style of colonisation in which ideals also played their part. In 1872 a special loan for Paraguay was negotiated in England for a group of farmers from Lincolnshire to settle near Asunción. Instead of farmers, however, the committee rounded up eight hundred 'needy artisans off the streets of London' and despatched them instead. No preparations had been made and, inevitably, over one hundred and fifty of them died of hunger and exposure. The survivors eventually made their way to Buenos Aires. Only two families stayed the course.

Another scheme was called 'New Australia'. This was the brainchild of William Lane, a journalist from England

who had made his home in Queensland. After the catas-
trophic collapse of a strike called by the Australian
Labour Federation, thousands of workers found themselves
with no means of livelihood and Lane suggested that they
could set up a labour utopia all their own in Paraguay. He
persuaded the government there to grant nearly half a
million acres to the New Australia Co-operative Settlement Association. The socialist-minded settlers gave all
their property to the association and pledged to stay teetotal
in the hope of 'showing the world that even [..] workers
can live a life worth living'. The first 250 sailed from
Sydney to Villarrica and began to construct a settlement.
However, some of them succumbed to the local drink,
Caña, and were kicked out by Lane. They were followed
by a number of others who succumbed to the hard work.
There were many grumbles. One of these was that the
women 'were positively afraid to face the nocturnal music
in their connubial tents'. A second batch of immigrants
arrived but the dissension in Nueva Australia was impossible to control and Lane moved away to begin another
colony in Cosmé. Co-operative ideals were eventually
abandoned and the immigrants bought their own land.
The settlement fell apart although there are still many
descendants in the area. There is no evidence the Försters
knew of these earlier attempts at utopianism.

Isolation was the name of the game. Cut off from the
rest of the continent, Paraguay changed little and this explains how the tiny racist colony of Germans founded by
Bernhard and Elizabeth could live hidden away in the
jungle for more than half a century. Their little utopia,
their New Germany, which would never suffer from the
canker of Jewish influence, trickled on forgotten by the
world it had left behind.
They had chosen only those who they considered to be
pure Arians, 'We will breed an Arian master-race here in

103

the forests of South America. I will lead you to a new fatherland. The old Germany is corrupt but our New Germany will last forever'. She was somewhat of a prophet as the little colony remains there today but its posthumous existence is not quite as she had dreamt it. Things are never as simple as idealism paints them.

This is what really happened.

Elizabeth met Bernhard at Bayreuth where he was attracted by Wagner's political writings rather than by his music. He had been trying to get into the Wagner circle for some time but had been ignored by Wagner. He and Elizabeth, however, had much in common. Both had Lutheran pastors as father's and both moved in the same circles. Both had widowed mothers who lived in Naumberg and knew each other. After the first of the first night's and the other two which followed, the Försters, mother and son, paid a visit to the Nietzsches, mother and daughter, who were at home to them in Naumberg. They talked about the tragic fall of Germany at the hands of the Jews and the possibility of a renaissance of the German spirit. Later Nietzsche received a letter from his sister, 'It was a real feast to listen to someone who speaks our language'. A proto-attempt at the royal plural and not the last. Elizabeth was ready for Bernhard's simple remedies and drank them up with a will.

Thus were Bernhard and Elizabeth drawn to each other by their views. Theirs was a true meeting of minds. Elizabeth was well into her thirties by then and had already refused more than enough suitable suitors to cause her mother to worry. Förster was, like the madman of Nietzsche's fable, a type whose time had not yet come but would, later, without him. A time, in fact, which seems to return eternally. He was 32 and a confirmed and quite fanatical anti-semite and pseudo-intellectual racist. He had been sucked into the Wagner cult and slavishly swallowed all Wagner's ideology without even chewing it. He was impressed by Bayreuth and the maestro. He wrote endless pamphlets echoing Wagner's arguments which were any-

104

way echoes of echoes. These ideas were his infallible guide to all the problems from which Germany was suffering and all the solutions to them. The problems were materialism and the worship of money for which the Jews and the Jesuits were responsible. The solution was the purification of the race which would free the blond blue-eyed Aryan hero to be himself and get rid of the virus which was staining his potential.

Wagner's subtle comments about the Jews began as early as 1850 when he wrote 'Judaism in Music'. He took his cue from good old Luther, 'Why is there an involuntary revulsion which is awakened by the person and character of the Jew? We deceive ourselves if we classify as bad manners any frank reference to our natural antipathy to the Jewish character [...] In the present state of things the Jew is more than free - he dominates and, as long as money continues to be the power which brings all our efforts to nothing, he will continue so to do'. Although his future father in law, Franz Liszt was horrified by it. Förster lapped it up.

Förster was a professional in the Jew baiting business. How did he go about it? This is how. He had emerged from an inn with a friend after drinking too much and they got into a tram. He then started to rant at some of the passengers whom he took for Jews. He pointed them out one at a time, mocking their semitic features in sham Yiddish and railing against the Jews, the Jewish press and Jewish business. His fellow passengers took objection and some of them, led by a Jewish businessman, manhandled him and his friend off the tram the better to argue on the pavement. This businessman began to take down the names of Förster and others with the intention of reporting them to the police. Förster's friend objected, 'But you're only a Jew', he shouted with the result that the businessman smashed him in the face. This resulted in general fisticuffs which were noticed by a passing policeman who dragged them all off to the police station. Förster's defence was that he was an Aryan by descent and that should be enough. He was, however, taken to court, fined ninety marks and reprimanded. The incident made him more of a figure than he had been before among certain sections of the community.

It was after this public brawl that he lost his teaching job, the authorities deciding that a man who started scuffles in public was an unsuitable example for the young.

Out of work, he had to look for some other occupation. His new-found notoriety enabled him to launch a petition which he presented to Bismarck. This petition called for the restriction of Jewish immigration and the cleansing of Jews from all positions of authority and influence. It even contained the suggestion that all German Jews should be made to register so that this demand could be more easily effected and further influxes of Jews be controlled. The petition managed to collect 267,000 signatures although it must be said that one person who refused to sign was Wagner. It may be asked why. Was this evidence of a lapse in his hatred of the Jews? Maybe at that time he needed the services of his many Jewish collaborators. The maestro wrote to one of them that 'I have nothing whatever to do with the current anti-semitic movements'. Note that crucial 'current'. The fact was that the 'current movements', those of Treitschke and Dühring or of Stöcker, were not radical enough for the maestro who no longer thought of the Jews as a racial threat but rather as the symbols and agents of degeneration in German life. Elizabeth, on the other hand, hardly thinking at all, was in this up to her elbows, toiling round Naumberg collecting signatures. Bismarck turned a blind eye to the petition but this didn't stop Förster and his colleagues founding the 'German Peoples' Party' which managed to attract over six thousand supporters to its first meeting. Only by joining together 'can we defeat the Jewish plague'. She didn't know of Wagner's opposition which never became public knowledge. Indeed, Förster never questioned anything coming from the Wagner oracle and he took Cosima as his symbol of the potential inherent in German womanhood which is exactly what she took herself to be even though she was illegitimate and an adulteress.

Förster latched on to almost all the expected tenets. He was against vivisection and inoculation. He supported homeopathy and the sanctity of the soil. He was a vegetarian. Familiar, all of these notions? He wrote a pamphlet on Jewry and German art and used as a frontispiece Dürer's 'Knight, Death and the Devil'. The Jews were 'besmirching German art with gold' and 'whoever becomes a traitor to the most holy German volk' should be 'hanged on a bare tree'.

Of course, you would expect Nietzsche to dislike his brother-in-law, 'This accursed anti-semitism is the cause of a radical break between me and my sister'. The two men met only once, at the celebration in Naumberg of Nietzsche's 41st birthday. They talked about sex and agreed that great men should be able to control their libidos and be masters of their senses. A bit sad really, Nietzsche on the recoil from his obsession with Lou Salomé and Förster newly married. But well.

Before leaving on his first trip to the Americas Cosima wrote that Wagner was alarmed at the plan and 'has no great confidence in it'. Förster, perhaps unluckily as things turned out, never saw the letter. Within the week Wagner was dead.

For Elizabeth, Bernhard was the man of action which Nietzsche would never be, 'I find Fritz more and more unsympathetic. I wish he shared Förster's views. Förster has ideas that will make men better and happier if they are promoted and carried out. Some day Förster will be praised as one of the best of Germans and a benefactor of his people'. How right she turned out to be! The comparison between the two men was apparent in everything.

107

Elizabeth was now a mature woman who was looking into the abyss of spinsterdom and it was obvious to Förster that she would be an ideal partner in his colonial schemes. So, although they were probably never in love with each other, they both saw the advantages of a merger.

In 1885, on Wagner's birthday, May 22nd, Elizabeth married Bernhard. Nietzsche spent the day at the Lido in Venice. Lo and behold, Dürer's etching, 'Night, Death and the Devil', turned up again. Nietzsche (conspicuously absent from the wedding) sent it as a present. Förster, turning Nietzsche's intention on its head, saw it as representing the German hero going into battle against the Jewish demon. Actually Dürer had painted it with a book of Erasmus in mind, one of his most popular texts called 'The Handbook of the Christian Knight'. In a letter about the woodcut Dürer had written, 'Oh Erasmus of Rotterdam when wilt thou take thy stand? Hark thou knight of Christ, ride forth at the side of Christ our Lord, protect the truth, obtain the martyr's crown'. This was probably not in the mind of Förster as he rode forth to the new world. It was certainly not in Erasmus' thoughts at all.

Earlier Nietzsche had written, 'Just such a Dürer knight was our Schopenhauer, lacking all hope yet willing the truth. There has been no other such as he'.

Oh for a paradise free of Jews where a new Germany could be built on those good old virtues of heroic vegetarianism and Aryanism. This was Förster's dream and he constructed it on the back of a popular movement in the Germany of the time where hundreds of societies bent on colonisation were being formed. The dream was millennial. It was founded on the conviction that the inhabitants of this new land were none other than the ten lost tribes of Israel whose conversion would lead to the end of the present era of misery and death and usher in the second coming.

To go to a country free of Jews and hunt up the lost ten tribes (all presumably Jewish) and convert them to anti-semitism. Thus to bring on the millennium, clean and Judenfrei (which meant much the same thing). Now there was an ideal worthy of a man like Förster and his helpmate! And Nietzsche knew what he thought of that, 'once again there appears that lust for power which, in times gone by, was inflamed by the belief that one was in possession of the truth and which bore such beautiful names that from then on one could venture to be inhuman with a good conscience (to burn Jews, heretics and good books and terminate entire higher cultures such as those of Peru and Mexico)'.

Of course the continent was as little Deutschfrei as it was Judenfrei. The place was swarming with both nations who were getting on pretty well together. But then Förster wasn't one to let mere facts sway his opinions. The time was still some way off when the thought would enter German minds that they could live Judenfrei at home, so off they went in their thousands to colonise other places.

In 1880 Wagner published a booklet on 'Religion and Art'. In section three he suggests that the degeneration of the human race has been brought about by its departure from its natural food. Thus 'its regeneration will depend upon renouncing a diet of meat' just as in American prisons where 'the greatest criminals have been trans-formed into the most gentle and upright of men by a wisely planned botanic diet'. He suggests 'a sensibly exec-uted transmigration to those quarters of our globe the rich fertility of which is adequate to support the present popul-ation of every country in the world, that is to say, the South American peninsular itself'. In such a racially pure German colony Jews would be banned and the place would be German, vegetarian, Teutonic and Lutheran. A Utopia in the midst of the burgeoning jungle which would provide all the food that they would need. Förster seized on Wagner's rantings as the verification of his dreams. After looking around he came to the conclusion that Paraguay was really the only place left and in 1883 he set off alone across the ocean to find a suitable site.

The couple worked hard to advance their ideals. Their propaganda began to have its effect and, by their first wedding anniversary, they had got together a band of pioneer settlers. These were either desperately poor or racist and anti-semitic or simply naive but one thing they all were was unequivocally Aryan. On February 15th 1887 the little band of colonists, consisting of fourteen families, clambered up the gangplank at Hamburg docks to board the steamship 'Uruguay'. Large crowds had gathered to see them off. But there was one face that was not gazing up and waving. Nietzsche couldn't bear to see his sister leave Germany, 'I have lost my sister. We are separated irrevocably. The convictions by which my brother-in-law is prepared to live and die are even more alien to me than Paraguay'. Wagner's telegram was short and to the point. It read 'Have a good trip'. However, in spite of the maestro's best wishes, their journey across the Atlantic was terrible. It took nearly five weeks. The boat was overcrowded and the weather very hot. They left the steamer at Montevideo and piled into a smelly, unstable river boat that took them up the Rio Parana to Asunción. More heat and danger and thick jungle on either side. At Asunción Elizabeth and her husband left the party which carried on up the Rio Paraguay to the north. They finally struggled out of the boat onto dry land and watched the lonely vessel chug away leaving them high and not so very dry in the midst of the jungle. They looked around them with disbelief.

'Nueva Germania', one hundred and fifty miles to the north of Asunción, was certainly new. It had never had any population to speak of and had been totally deserted for some time. It didn't take the new colonists long to realise that things were going to be far from easy. As is so very often the case, the difference between the propaganda and the reality was dramatic. Being mostly townspeople they would have had some difficulty in adapting to any kind of country life but were quite unprepared for the cloud of problems which faced them in their new jungle setting.

Diseases for which they were unprepared and for which there was no cure spread remorselessly through the group, none of whom had the immunity of the local population. The swarms of sub-tropical insects proved fatal on more than one occasion. There were also deaths from fleas, worms and lice. On top of this, few of the colonists had any knowledge of farming and were unable to cope with the soil which was like clay, too solid to get a plough through without strenuous effort. The only real crop they were able to grow was a sturdy root called manioc. This formed almost their entire botanic diet.

Meanwhile Elizabeth and Förster were at Asunción, living somewhat more comfortably in a hotel. Elizabeth only came to join the colonists when they had finished the construction of a house suitable to her position. 'Förster-hof', her large colonial mansion, stood out in the jungle setting. It had a huge salon and a suite of other rooms. The whole was furnished well and conformed to the best taste of the time. It had a high roof and stone floors. There was even a piano. Furniture was shipped in from Europe and labour from miles around. In her letters home, Elizabeth boasted of the number of servants she had in the house.

When she arrived, her new Germans came down to the jetty to greet her, 'May God grant that all future colonists look as decent as the ones standing there. They all have such honest faces. Here in the primal forest we are feasting on compassion, heroic self-denial, Christianity and Aryanism. Accompanied by the strains of 'Deutschland Über Alles', I finally set foot on the soil of the New Germany. With a speech of welcome one colonist raised his glass and shouted "Long live the mother of the colony" which pleased my heart'.

Although, for most of the colonists, day to day existence was a rigorous fight to stay alive, Elizabeth wrote with her usual verve, 'What an opportunity we are offering Ger-

111

man workers who are withering away in poverty, sickness and despair in many parts of the old fatherland. What an idyllic picture this makes. Nothing is alien. No. Everything is homely and German'. Förster advised the new colonists to bring with them 'Courage and resignation, strength and fortitude. Moral fibre from the old fatherland to bestow upon the next generation'.

Imagine the two of them, walking there among the fronds, seeking the shadows to shelter them from the relentless truth of the midday sun, burning, burning. Surrounded by one thing and yet imagining, yearning for something quite different. Paradoxes. Impossible to return to Germany as the money had all run out. Stuck in a wilderness of rats, snakes and goodness knows what else, they were condemned by Elizabeth's determination to lead an idyllic and idealistic existence.

It was then that Förster started to call her Eli for short. Which is, of course, one of the names of God and attached as a coda to the names of the archangels. Also, appropriately, the name of the man who first made himself judge over Israel.

But the dream had begun to collapse almost immediately. Early fervour had already been cooled by the horrors of the journey and the place itself offered little relief. The colonists had been carefully prepared for something quite different. They were ready enough, even eager, to work to achieve an ideal but, struggle as they might, they could hardly produce enough to survive. It wasn't long before they began to turn against the Försters. Elizabeth was cold and aloof and clearly more concerned with her reputation in Germany than she was with the colonists. Dear Bernhard was hardly ever there. He spent his time in Asunción desperately despatching letters pleading for more loans and contributions to pay off the huge sums he had borrowed from the Paraguayan government to keep the colony running. Every now and then he would appear without warning, stay for a few days, and then disappear again.

The colony was clearly up against it. Some of the colonists were leaving and any new ones who arrived, attracted by Elizabeth's imaginative articles in the German press, were rapidly disillusioned. And what about the ability to deceive which seems to have come so easily to her? As she looked around her, did she really see what she was putting down in her letters? And later, did she really believe, as she slaved over her editions of her brother's books and reinvented his philosophy, that she was 'completing his work'? Her lust for power transformed the world she saw and heard, the very taste and smell of it. It had to be as she wanted it to be and so it was. The resurrection of corpses.

Förster had written failure into the agreement he had signed with the Paraguayan government on 17th November 1886. He had accepted a lease for a mere two years and agreed that the land would only become the property of the colonists if they could produce 140 families by the end of the period. If not, then the lease would end and the land return to the government. On top of this he would be obliged to give back to the colonists all the costs they had incurred as well as the money they had paid him for the land on the assumption that they would eventually own it. Förster, having the optimism of the fanatic, perhaps genuinely thought all this was possible. They managed the 40 but the 100 escaped them. And even some of the 40 had given up. Förster was in debt up to his eyeballs. He went on dreaming until one of the colonists took matters into his own hands. This man was Julius Klingbeil. He came, saw and was conquered by the inhospitable environment and rapidly realised that the Försters were taking everyone for a ride. He returned, like so many others, to Germany but, unlike the rest, didn't quietly vanish back into the undergrowth. He produced a book, 'Revelations Concerning Bernhard Förster's Colony New Germany', which went into great detail about the questionable goings-on in 'Nueva Germania'. He accused Förster of stealing the colonists' cash, of telling them lies and acting as a kind of tyrant insisting that the poor colonists buy everything they needed through him at higher prices than they could buy them elsewhere and live in shacks while the Försters, man and wife, acted like petty lord-lings and lived in a grand house full of all the luxuries which they could bring out of Germany or buy in the Americas. He was less severe on Förster than on his wife who, he alleged, lorded it over her husband in much the same way as he lorded it over the colonists. And as they lor-ded it over the poor natives. Caste once again. Nietzsche wrote to Overbeck, 'Things in Paraguay are as bad as they could be. The Germans tempted over there are rebelling and claiming their money back and there is none. There ha-ve already been acts of violence. I fear the worst'.

Klingbeil's book was condemned as a libel in the 'Bay-reuther Blätter' but this hardly effected the disastrous situation which was now common knowledge back in the fatherland. Förster's stream of funds, already shallow, finally dried up altogether. This was the beginning of the end for Förster. By the closing months of 1889, he had left 'Nueva Germania' for the last time and gone to ground at the Hotel del Lago near Asunción where he was regularly more drunk than alive. In a note to Elizabeth he wrote, 'What will become of us?' On the morning of June 3rd the maid who opened the door to his bedroom was hit by a strong chemical stench and soon spotted the rapidly stiffening corpse on the bed. Förster had poisoned himself with a lethal mixture of strychnine and morphine which he may have downed while still effected by a long evening at the bar which was only the last of a six week bout of drinking.

Elizabeth would never admit that her husband had been a failure. She began to resurrect him within hours of his death. Rushing to Asunción, she managed to pers-uade a Paraguayan medic to sign a death certificate that gave the cause of death as 'a nervous attack'. Her version was that his death had been a tragedy for the colony and that 'if Förster had not died so young, the colony would have been all that he planned - that, with his notable gifts for colonising, he would have achieved everything that he had hoped to accomplish for the glory of Germany'. She later recalled that her husband had spent his last hours in the company of a Spanish priest, presumably in converse about matters philosophical, when he 'suddenly got up from his chair saying he felt ill and faint and telling the priest that he thought he was getting a nervous fever'. He then sat down again holding his head in one hand and pressing the other to his heart. After what seemed like a re-covery, he lay down to sleep. Sadly his condition worsened and the fatal attack came on the night of 3rd June. She wrote that 'false friends and the schemes of his enemies had broken his heart'. Thus it was that such a valuable life ended. He had become 'a hero of battles worthy of Valhalla, whose face is an icon of the true Christ united with the pure German race, who fell on a foreign field for his belief in the German spirit'.

To escape the Jews Förster had gone to Eldorado, and run out of money; had glimpsed Utopia and had run out of dreams. Suicide was his replacement therapy. Of a fairly drastic kind. His problem was that he went to a continent that had already been comprehensively raped of its wealth and made unerringly for the one part of it where the sticky clay had never contained any precious metal in the first place. Also, had he only but known it, he went to a continent that had its fair share of Jews. They had made their way there four hundred years earlier to escape the terrible persecutions of the inquisition back in their Euro-pean homelands where they had been forcibly christianised. These conversos escaped to the New World to rid them-selves of ever present further persecution. Amongst other things, they were the traders, the wheeler-dealers of the New World. It was they who made the place tick. The fact that the inquisition followed them didn't deter this influx. Quite possibly, some of the conquistadors were themselves conversos. It may even have been that Aleixo Garcia himself, the man who opened up the heart of the continent to another cycle of conversion of its hidden Jews, of the last remaining remnants of the lost ten tribes, was himself a Jew.

Förster's death was the second piece of bad news to reach Elizabeth within days. She had just received word that her brother's mind had gone and that he had been taken to the asylum at Jena. It is not only in mathematics that two minuses make a plus. Things in the colony were getting dangerous. Her colonists were writing to the 'Chemnitz Colonial Society' with a stream of complaints, most of them directed against their mentor. The society decided that the colony would be best served by the removal of Elizabeth. Her husband's death and the news of her brother's madness gave her the excuse she so desperately needed and she stayed on just long enough to rearrange her husband's suicide and then took the boat out, leaving her followers to fend for themselves as best they could .

She moved quite naturally from one fantasy to another, 'I must now bid farewell to colonial affairs. Now another great task demands all my life's time and energy. The care of my dear and only brother, the philosopher Nietzsche, the protection of his works and the description of his life and thought'. When she arrived at Naumberg station Nietzsche was waiting to greet her. He had been brought there by his mother and when Elizabeth alighted from the train, the limp figure was pushed gently forward to meet the sister he no longer recognised.

PART III

Madness

Raskolnikov dreamt a terrible dream [...] some peasant's small, lean, greyish-brown mare was harnessed to one of these huge carts, the sort of poor old nag which - he had seen it so often - found it very hard to draw quite an ordinary cart with wood or hay piled on top of it, especially when the cart was stuck in the mud or in a rut, and every time that happened, the peasant flogged her so brutally, so brutally, sometimes even across the eyes and muzzle, and he felt so sorry, so sorry for the poor old horse that he almost burst into tears, and his mother always used to take him away from the window. But now in front of the pub pandemonium suddenly broke loose. A crowd of blind drunk big peasants in red and blue shirts with their coats thrown over their shoulders came out of the pub, yelling and singing, and strumming their balalaikas. 'Come on, get on my cart!' shouted one of them, quite a young peasant with a terribly thick neck and a very red, beefy face. 'I'll drive you all home! Get in!'

But almost immediately there was a loud outburst of laughter and shouts.

'Look at that old nag of his! Drive us all home, will he?'

'Have you lost your senses Mikolka? What made you put such an old weed in a big cart like that?'

'The mare is twenty if she's a day, lads!'

117

Come on! I'll drive you all home!' Mikolka shouted again, jumping into the cart before everyone else, picking up the reins, and standing, drawn up to his full height, in front. 'Matvey has taken the bay', he shouted from the cart, 'and this old nag of mine, lads, is just breaking my heart. I should have cut her throat long ago. Doesn't earn her keep, she doesn't. Come on, I say. Get in, get in, all of you. I'll make her jump. I'll make her go a-galloping all the way. You'll see. She'll go a-galloping all the way!' and he took the whip in his hands, preparing himself gleefully to whip the little grey-brown mare.

'Come along, let's get in!' laughing voices were raised in the crowd. 'D'you hear? He'll make her go a-galloping all the way!'

'I bet you she's never gone a-galloping for ten years or more'.

'She'll be skipping along!'

'Don't spare her lads! Take you whips, all of you! Ready-y?

'Aye, serves her right! Give her a good flogging!'

The prisoner called up had to run full force and stand in front of the authorities; after a short talk of a few seconds he had to pull down his trousers and, exposing his buttocks, lie down on the beams. One of the SS men pressed with his boot on the head of the culprit so as to immobilise him. Two SS men with long whips stood on both sides of the punished and the blows were dealt, in turns, form one side and then the other. The SS men counted aloud as they beat him, resting for a few seconds before each blow. Red bruises appeared on the buttocks side by side, and crossing, until blood started to gush. The victim yelled, which led to stronger pressure of the boot on his head, and sometimes a kick. The SS men did not like to have their solemn ceremony interrupted by whimpering.

After some dozen blows, a victim ceased to whimper and his body, shrieking after each blow, became numb. Some inmates evacuated their bowels after several blows. After the predefined number of blows had been dealt and counted, when the SS man shouted 'Raus! Los!' (Out! Go!) the victim had to quickly pull up his trousers and run back to the rows. If the punished inmate did not stand up, due to fainting or exhaustion, he received several kicks in the head and then a Gnadenschuss (mercy shot) - a shot in the back of the head from the SS man's pistol.

> They all got into Mikolka's cart, laughing and joking. Six men clambered into the cart, and there was still room for more. They took a fat, red-cheeked peasant woman with them [...] In the crowd people were laughing, and indeed how could they help laughing? The mare was all skin and bones, and there she was supposed to drag such a heavy load at a gallop! Two young lads in the cart at once took a whip each and got ready to help Mikolka. There was a shout, 'Gee-up!' and the poor mare started pulling away with all her might, but far from galloping, could scarcely manage to move the cart one step at a time, working away helplessly with her legs, snorting and cowering under the blows of the three whips which were belabouring her mercilessly. The laughter in the cart and in the crowd was redoubled, but Mikolka was beginning to lose his temper, and, in his fury, he showered blow and blow in the helpless mare, as though he really thought that she could gallop.
>
> 'Let me lend you a hand, lads,' a young fellow in the crowd cried, his fingers itching to have a go at the old mare.
>
> 'Come on! Get in, all of you! Mikolka shouted, 'she'll take you all! I'll flog the life out of her!' and he went on flogging and flogging, in his blind fury hardly knowing what to hit her with.

Then we went to work. In our wooden shoes we were chased by blows from rods into a corner of the field and had to fill sometimes our caps, at other times our jackets, with stones, wet sand or mud, and, holding them with both hands and running under a hail of blows, bring them to the opposite corner of the field, empty the stuff, refill it and bring it back to the opposite corner, and so on. A gauntlet of screaming SS men and privileged pris-

119

oners armed with rods and whips, let loose on us a hail of blows. It was hell.

> 'Daddy! Daddy!' he cried to his father. 'Daddy, look what they are doing! Daddy, they're beating the poor little horse!' [...] He tore himself out of his father's hands and, hardly realising what he was doing, ran to the old horse. But the poor old mare was already in a very bad state. She was gasping for breath, standing still, pulling at the cart again, and almost collapsing in the read.
>
> 'Flog her to death!' shouted Mikolka. 'I don't mind. I'm going to flog her to death myself! [...]

At the marketplace, the Jews, who had been forced to squat for hours were mocked and kicked, and some of the Germans organised a game of tossing apples and whoever was struck by the apple was then killed. This sport was continued at the railway station, this time with empty liquor bottles. Bottles were tossed over Jewish heads and whoever was struck by a bottle was dragged out of the crowd and beaten murderously amid roaring laughter. Then some of those who were thus mangled were shot.

> A loud peal of laughter suddenly drowned everything unable to stand the rain of blows from the whips any longer, the poor beast started kicking helplessly. [...] such a bag of bones, and there she was kicking!
>
> Two lads in the crowd also armed themselves with whips and ran to the mare, intending to flog her from each side. They ran to take up their positions.
>
> 'Whip her across the muzzle!' shouted Mikolka. 'Across the eyes! Whip her across the eyes!'
>
> 'Let's have a song, lads!' someone in the cart shouted, and everyone in the cart took up the cry. They started singing a boisterous song, a tambourine tinkled, and there was shrill whistling during the refrains. [...]
>
> He ran beside the old mare, he ran in front of her, he saw her being whipped across her eyes, across the very

eyes! He was crying. His heart heaved. Tears rolled down his cheeks. One of the men who were flogging the horse grazed his face with the whip, but he felt nothing. Wringing his hands and screaming, he rushed up to the old man with the grey beard who was shaking his head and condemning it all. A woman took him by the hand and tried to lead him away, but he freed himself and ran back to the poor old horse, which seemed to be at the last gasp, but started kicking once more.

'Oh, to hell with you!' shouted Mikolka furiously, and, throwing down his whip, he bent down and dragged out a long, thick shaft from the bottom of the cart. Taking hold of it by one end with both hands, he swung it with an effort over the grey-brown mare.

'He'll strike her dead!' they shouted all round.

'He'll kill her!'

'My property!' shouted Mikolka, and let fall the shaft with all his might. There was the sound of a heavy thud.

The men of Police Battalion 309's First and Third Companies drove their victims into the synagogue, the less compliant Jews receiving liberal blows of encouragement. The Germans packed the large synagogue full. The fearful Jews began to chant and pray loudly. After spreading gasoline around the building, the Germans set it ablaze; one of the men tossed an explosive through the window to ignite the holocaust. The Jews' prayers turned into screams. A battalion member described the scene, 'I saw [...] smoke that came out of the synagogue and heard there how the incarcerated people cried loudly for help. I was about seventy metres from the synagogue. I could see the building and observed that people tried to escape through the windows. One shot at them [...] One of the men of the Battalion shouted 'Let it burn, it's a nice little fire, it's great fun'.

'Flog her! Flog her! Why have you stopped?' shouts were heard in the crowd.

And Mikolka swung the shaft another time, and another terrific blow fell across the back of the unhappy mare. She subsided on her haunches, but presently was on her feet

121

again, pulling, pulling with all her remaining strength first on one side and then on another, trying to move the cart. But they were belabouring her from every side with six whips, and the shaft was raised again and fell for the third and then for the fourth time, slowly and with terrific force. Mikolka was furious because he had not been able to kill her with one blow.

'Alive and kicking!' they shouted on all sides.

'Bet she'll fall down any minute now, lads,' shouted a sportsman in the crowd. 'She's about finished!'

'Why don't you strike her with an axe? Despatch her at once!' a third one shouted.

'Oh damn her! Make way! Mikolka yelled furiously and, throwing down the shaft, he once more bent down in the cart and pulled out an iron bar. 'Mind!' he shouted, swinging it with all his might over his poor old horse. The bar came down with a crash; the old mare swayed, subsided, and was about to give another pull at the cart when the bar once again descended on her back with terrific force and she collapsed on the ground as though her four legs had given way from under her all at once.

From Warsaw, 'Today is the great day. The weather is pleasant. The sun is shining brightly. Untersturmfuehrer Handtke wipes the sweat from his fat, red face. Then he wipes his neck and gets ready again for action. He lashes out again with the whip and strikes the terrified victims on their heads and faces and any other part of the body he can reach'.

'Finish her off!' Mikolka shouted, jumping down from the cart, blind with rage.

A few young men, also red-faced and drunk, seized whatever they could lay their hands on - whips, sticks, the shaft - and ran to the dying mare. Mikolka stood on one side and started raining blows across her back with the iron bar without bothering to see where the blows were falling. The mare stretched out her head, heaved a deep sigh, and died.

'Settled her!' they shouted in the crowd.

'Why didn't she gallop?'

'My property!' shouted Mikolka, iron bar in hand and with blood-shot eyes. He stood there as though he were sorry he had nothing more to flog. [...]

But by now the poor little boy was beside himself. He pushed his way through the crowd to the grey-brown mare, put his arms round her dead, bloodstained muzzle, and kissed her, kissed her on the eyes, on the lips

On the morning of January 3rd, as he was leaving the house, Nietzsche saw an old nag being brutally beaten by its cabman in the Piazza at the end of the street. Overcome with pity for the beaten horse, he broke into tears, staggered across the square and flung his arms around the poor animal's neck in an attempt to protect it. Then he collapsed onto the ground sobbing. The inevitable small crowd of curious onlookers collected around him but little was done until his landlord, Davide Fino, passing by on the other side of the street, saw the little huddle of people and joined them out of curiosity. He instantly recognised his lodger huddled on the ground clutching himself around the shoulders and weeping quietly. With some difficulty he managed to stand him up, extricate him from the crowd and half carry him to the house and on up to his room.

Nietzsche's health was to be suffered and overcome.

He sent his CV to Georg Brandes, 'Around 1876 my health got worse. I then spent a winter in Sorrento with my old friend Baroness Meysenbug and the congenial Dr Rée. I didn't improve. An extremely persistent and agonising pain in the head exhausted all my energies. For several

123

interminable years it got worse reaching a peak of constantly recurring pain of which I had two hundred days of suffering a year. The illness must have had a purely localised source, there being no neurological basis for it whatsoever. I have never had any symptoms of mental disorder, not even fever or fainting fits. My pulse at that time was as slow as the first Napoleon's (60). My speciality was resisting this extreme pain for two of three days at a stretch, remaining alert and fully lucid, though I was continuously spitting up mucus. There was a rumour going around that I was in a lunatic asylum (and that I had even died there). Nothing could be further from the truth. On the contrary it was during that time that I came to full maturity'.

He wrote to Rohde, 'My physical condition still leaves much to be desired [...] Oh how I yearn for good health! One must have an undertaking which one expects to outlast one's own lifetime to be really grateful for each good night's sleep, for each warm ray of sunshine, yes even for "regularity". As it is, my lower internal organs seem to be ruined. Hence the bad nerves, insomnia, haemorrhoids and coughing up blood, etc'.

Letter to Richard Wagner, 'My neuralgia gets to work so thoroughly, so scientifically, that it actually conducts experiments to see how much pain I can endure, and each time takes thirty hours to do the job. Every four to eight days I can depend on a repetition of this research. It's a scholar's disease, you see. Until now my highly problematic reflecting and writing has always made me ill'.

But then again to Rohde, 'The way I live now I can endure the worst of my afflictions for between them there are so many happy peals of thought and feeling'.

To Peter Gast, 'I have been putting my plan to do without thinking into practice. And with good reason since "behind every thought prowls the devil" of a furious attack of pain. The manuscript you received of 'The Wanderer and his Shadow' was purchased at such expense that no one would have written it at that price had he been able to do otherwise. Even now I tremble when I recall it.

To Dr Otto Eiser, 'My existence is a terrible burden. I would long ago have given it up were it not for my having done the most revealing psychological and moral research in exactly this state of suffering and almost absolute renunciation. My joyous thirst for knowledge brings me to heights where I can conquer all distress and despair. On the whole I am happier than ever before in my life. And yet! constant pain, for several hours each day a feeling something like seasickness, a semi-paralysis which makes speaking difficult and, for a change of pace, furious seizures (the last involving vomiting for three days and nights; I lusted for death). To be unable to read! And only just able to write! No human contact! No Music!'

To Paul Rée, 'My health is too shattered and my misery too constant. All this self overcoming, all this endurance - what good has it ever done me?'

To Gast, 'One day in ten is a good one; that is par for the course, the devil take it!'

To Overbeck, 'Since I left Turin I have been in terrible shape. Constant headaches, constant vomiting; all my old ills are back again, wrapped up in a nervous exhaustion that makes the entire machine useless. I am having trouble warding off the most depressing of thoughts. Clearheaded as I am, I cannot choose but be pessimistic about my condition as a whole. Not only health but its prerequisite is missing. My vital energy is impaired. The ravages of ten years and more have taken their irreparable toll. All this time I have lived solely off my 'capital' and put nothing, absolutely nothing, back [...] I am not suffering from a disease of the brain or of the stomach but the pressure of nervous exhaustion - in part hereditary (from my father who died solely of the after-effects of a general want of energy) in part hard-earned - which manifests itself in countless ways'.

'For fourteen years I have not had a day's real health. I have woken up sick and gone to bed weary; and I have done my work with perseverance. I have written in bed, and written out of it, written with haemorrhages, written

125

in sickness, written torn apart by coughing, written when my head was swimming with weakness; and for so long, it seems to me, that I have won my wager and recovered my gauntlet. I am better now and have been, rightly speaking, since I came to the Pacific; and still, few are the days when I am not in some physical distress. And the battle goes on - ill or well, is a trifle; just as long as it goes on. I was made for a contest'. Indeed, this illness 'has been of the very greatest help to me; it has set me free. It has restored to me the courage to be myself'.

We have a picture of Nietzsche from Stephan Zweig who wrote of the non-Jewish wanderer's life that he would 'go into the small, narrow, modest, coldly furnished chambre garnie where innumerable notes, pages, writings and proofs are piled up on the table, but no flowers, no decoration, scarcely a book and hardly ever a letter. Off in a corner, a heavy and graceless wooden trunk, his only possession, with the two shirts and the other worn suit. Apart from this, only books and manuscripts, and on a tray countless bottles, jars and potions against the migraines, which often render him all but senseless for hours, against his stomach cramps and his spasmodic vomiting, against the slothful intestines. Above all, there are the dreadful sedatives against his insomnia, chloral hydrate and Veronal, a frightening arsenal of poisons and drugs which are his only relief in the empty silence of this hostile room in which he never rests except in brief and artificially conquered sleep. Wrapped in his overcoat and a woollen scarf (for the wretched stove smokes but gives no warmth), his fingers freezing, his double glasses pressed close to the paper, his hurried hand writes for hours - words the dim eyes can hardly decipher. For hours he sits like this and writes until his eyes burn'.

And on to a few words about Nietzsche's eyesight.

At Pforta 'Nobody showed much concern for Nietzsche's

eyesight. The place was dim with thick walls and few windows and there was little light during the day. In the evening the boys had to work by the light of little oil-lamps. As well as reading glasses Nietzsche needed dark glasses to protect his eyes from the sun'. He wrote home that he needed 'above all a strong pair of spectacles - send them to me as quickly as possible'.

By 1877 his sight had deteriorated so badly that his eyes had to be within about two inches of the paper he was writing on. His physician, Eiser, arranged a joint consultation in Frankfurt with the ophthalmologist Otto Kruger. Their verdict was that the headaches were due partly to severe damage sustained by the retinas in both eyes - choroidoretinitis is frequently syphilitic in origin - and partly to 'a predisposition in the irritability of the central organ', originating from excessive mental activity.

His eyes were still worrying him, however ruthlessly he ignored the pain while working, 'Sooner or later my eyes will function only in the shade of forests' and, he noted, 'eyes painful'.

Lou Salomé wrote that Nietzsche's eyes were 'not the eyes of so many short-sighted people, they did not blink or stare at you or embarrass you by coming up too close. They seemed rather like the defenders and guardians of his own treasures, silent mysteries upon which no uninvited glance was allowed to fall. His defective eyesight gave his features a unique kind of magic as they only reflected that which flowed deep inside his being rather than of the changing external impressions. Those eyes looked at the same time both into the interior and into the distance far beyond immediate objects. To put this better, the interior was like the distance'.

And from Elizabeth, 'Among the immediate causes of his insanity I include the enormous strain both on his intellect and on his short-sighted eyes. When we look at the notes and the manuscripts for that tremendous output from June to December 1888 and consider how carefully he read the proofs in order to make further corrections, we are inclined to ask ourselves how he managed to get through the work at all. Those who are not short-sighted cannot understand how terribly tiring it is to write under such conditions. After a time the stooping position comes to have a harmful effect on the nerves in the head and the stomach. There are no kind of spectacles which allows one to hold one's head up; the lens which my brother really ought to have worn makes the writing appear so small that it is of no use. It seems to me that this strain to his eye and neck muscles must be a contributory cause'.

Thus his impossible handwriting. He wrote with his thick glasses so close to the paper that his nose almost rubbed the page. As his sight deteriorated so did his writing until it became quite impossible to decipher. Peter Gast was the only man capable of making anything out of this illegible scrawl and spent endless hours making neat copies for the printer.

The overcoming of Nietzsche's health took a strange form. For the last few months of 1888 he stayed in Turin. He found the place congenial and had decided to make it his permanent residence. He was staying in a five storey house in the Via Carlo Alberto. His window looked out onto the road from the third floor. He had been deeply engrossed in his work but towards the end of the year his behaviour became a little strange. He drank more and more water, sometimes managing to down four carafes at a time. He went for long walks on his own, deeply submerged in thought as always. He was seen outside Rosenberg and Selliers, the bookshop, looking for new titles although he had no money to buy them. He spent time arguing about the price of fruit at the greengrocer's. He would extemporise for long hours at the piano. None of this, of course was that much out of the ordinary for Nietzsche but a thread of euphoria was beginning to appear.

De Chirico writes that, for Nietzsche, Turin 'is the Italian city par excellence'. In his memoirs he tells us, 'The true novelty discovered by this philosopher [...] is based on the atmosphere (atmosphere in the moral sense) [...] of an autumn afternoon, when the sky is clear and the shadows are longer than in summer, for the sun is beginning to be lower. This extraordinary sensation can be found in Italian cities and in Mediterranean cities like Genoa or Nice; but the Italian city par excellence where this extraordinary phenomenon appears is Turin'. Nietzsche's letters from there are full of strange contentment which have not been found before. The city is beneficial and superb. The people strangely kind and helpful. For them he holds a perfect fascination, 'Everyone glances at me as if I were a prince. There is special distinction in the way doors are held open and meals are placed before me'. He was convinced that the waiters were choosing him the best of the food and that the women at the market were selling him the choicest grapes at the lowest price. He began to write chapters with titles such as 'Why I am so clever', 'Why I am so wise' and 'Why I write such good books'. His strength was becoming phenomenal, otherworldly. He could do anything. He wrote that, 'on questions of decadence I am the highest court of appeal on earth. The most unheard of tasks are as easy as a game' and he could add that, 'quite literally I hold the future of the human race in the palm of my hand'.

To Gast, 'Turin is perfect, a splendid and singularly comforting place. It is a handsome and important city, full of fine squares and palaces. The population is 270,000. Many princes have their seats here and it is the headquarters of the general staff. There is a university and twelve theatres, some of them excellent. The bookshops have a good selection of books in three languages. Its chief pride is its splendid, spacious porticoes and colonnades, more splendid than anything of its kind in all the rest of Europe. These colonnades shelter you against all weathers and the marble and other stone is so clean and

129

beautiful that you feel you are in a drawing room. The air here is splendid, drier than I have found in any other city; it is very exhilarating, and gives one a tremendous appetite. This is because the high mountains are so close by. On three sides you can see the snow-capped Alps. Even from the centre of the city you can get a view of a world of mighty peaks'. It is 'the only town that I care to live in. It seems impossible that I could find such quiet and solitude amid wonderfully broad and beautiful streets in the best part of a metropolis, right near the centre'.

To Gast, 'I just looked at myself in the mirror and saw something completely new, a man in excellent spirits, well fed and ten years younger than he has any right to look [...] Days and days go by all equally perfect, full of sunshine. Magnificent trees glowing with gold, the sky and the wide river a pale blue and the air as pure as possible - a Claude Lorraine beyond all my dreams. As to the fruit, grapes of the tawniest sweetness and cheaper than in Venice! In every way this is a good place to live.

To his mother, 'We still have an abundance of the finest grapes, A pound of the very best quality costs 24 pfennigs. The food is incredibly wholesome and good. It's not for nothing that I live in the most famous cattle raising country and in its royal seat at that. The tenderness of the veal is simply a revelation to me, as is the delicious lamb I love so much. And what cooking! What a sensible, simple, even subtle cuisine! Until now I never knew what a good appetite could be. Honestly, I eat four times as much as in Nice, pay less, and haven't had a bit of indigestion. Granted that in this and other ways I am singled out for special favours. I certainly get the choicest morsels. But this is the case wherever I go - I am accepted as someone very distinguished. You would be astonished with what pride and dignity your old child swaggers around here.... '

To Overbeck, 'I cannot find any bad news to tell you about myself. Things are going ahead in a tempo fortissimo of hard work and high spirits. [...] Meanwhile I am getting rave reviews for my 'Wagner Case'. Not only is it being hailed as a psychological masterpiece of the first order, in an area no one had previously explored - the psychology of the musician - but they are saying that my analysis of the fundamentally decadent nature of German music is an event in the history of our culture which I alone could have brought off [...] Other good news as well. The most eminent Swedish writer, August Strindberg, whom Dr Brandes calls a 'real Genius', has now spoken out in my favour. And St Petersburg's high society is trying to establish relations with me, although greatly handicapped by the suppression of my works'.

To Carl Fuchs, 'In the years ahead there will be in utter confusion in the world. Since the old God has abdicated, I shall rule from now on'.

Another to his mother, 'Your poor old child is now a supremely famous man. Not especially in Germany - as the Germans are too stupid and vulgar for the grandeur of my genius and have always made themselves ridiculous where I am concerned - but everywhere else. I have only the most select admirers, highly placed and influential people in St Petersburg, Paris, Stockholm, Vienna and New York. Oh, if you only knew with what words the most important personages in the world express their devotion to me - the most charming women, not excluding a certain Madame la Princess Tenichev. There are true geniuses among my admirers. No name is treated with as much deference and distinction as mine is today... '

To Overbeck, 'In two months I shall be the foremost name on earth [...] It is amazing the utter fascination that I exert here in Turin, even though I am the most unassuming person and demand nothing. When I enter a large store the expression on everyone's face changes, women stare at me on the pavement, my street vendor saves the sweetest grapes for me and has even reduced the price! It was ridiculously low to begin with. [...] My waiters are splendidly polite and helpful [..] Nothing happens by chance any more. Whenever I think of someone a letter from him arrives obligingly at my door'.

To Meta von Salis, 'The year which is just ending has been too good [..] Meanwhile, in an entirely incredible way, I am beginning to become famous. I doubt any mortal has ever received letters of the kind I am getting now, all from the élite of the intellectual world, whose characters have stood the test of high office and positions. They come from everywhere, not least from the finest society in St Petersburg. And the French! You should hear the tone of M. Taine's letters to me. Just now a charming, perhaps charmed, message came from one of the foremost and most influential men in France, who proposes to interest himself in the publication and translation of my works - none other than the editor-in-chief of the 'Journal des Debates' and the 'Revue des Deux Mondes', Monsieur Bourdeau ... '

Although there may be reason for all this over-obliging behaviour. Nietzsche notes, 'I play so many silly tricks on myself and my head is so full of clownish private jokes that sometimes for half an hour in full view of everybody I will grin - I cannot think of a better word'. And again, 'I have just returned from a great concert [..] I was trying to recover from my extreme joy and my face was smirking continuously - once, tearfully , for ten whole minutes'.

At least for a moment he felt accepted for what he was, an interregnum of fame and health which has to be grasped for as long as possible even if it leads to a posthumous existence in which sickness and neglect can be forgotten.

After Davide had persuaded him back to his flat he lay for a long time unconscious on his bed and, when he finally came round, it was clear that he was no longer the old Nietzsche. He dashed around the room, dancing and singing, stopping every now and then to thump unmusically on the piano. Poor Fino, who had already summoned a doctor, now threatened to call in the police. This had the desired effect and Nietzsche began to calm down. He sat at his desk and started scratching away. He wrote to most of the courts of Europe telling them that he would be on his way to Rome on the following Tuesday and instructing them to be there to meet with him and the Pope. He wrote to 'dear Umberto', the king of Italy, and to the house of Baden, 'my children', to tell them of his plans. He sent a note to the Vatican Secretary of State telling the Pope to expect him. There was one exception to this general invitation and that was the Hohenzollerns. He advised the courts of the other German princes to have nothing to do with them for the Reich was still the enemy of German culture.

He wrote to Peter Gast a single line, 'To my Maestro Pietro. Sing me a new song. the world is transfigured and all the heavens rejoice'. He signed it 'The Crucified'. To Brandes went another letter of one line, 'After you had discovered me it was not hard to find me. The problem now is to lose me'. This also he signed 'the Crucified'. He wrote a string of letters to Strindberg, to Malwida, to Spit-teler, to Rohde, to Bülow. Cosima Wagner received an-other note of one line 'Ariadne, I love you'. This he signed 'Dionysus'.

One of the letters to Strindberg was written in Latin and Greek and opened, suspiciously, with a quotation from a Poem of Anacreon, 'I want, I want to be mad' and closed with the words 'It is a joy to be mad'.

At his desk writing intensely. To Burckhardt went an-other letter with the signature of Dionysus which was followed by another, longer letter of four pages, to which extra lines were scratched in the margins, 'I would much rather have been a professor at Basle than God; but I did not dare to carry my private egotism so far as to neglect the creation of the world. You see, one must make sacrifices. The remainder for Frau Cosima... Ariadne... There is magic from time to time... I have had Caiaphas put in chains; and last year I was crucified by the German doc-tors in a very long drawn-out manner. Wilhelm, Bismarck and all anti-semites abolished'.

Burckhardt got his letter in the post on the Sunday 6th January. The retired Basle professor of art struggled for some time with the minuscule and almost illegible scrawl in which it was written and soon realised that something had changed. One sentence which was added in the margin of the first page may have sounded to him like a not so crazy appeal for help, 'You can make any use of this letter which will not lower me in the estimation of the people of Basle'. Burckhardt put the letter carefully in his coat pocket and started out on the short walk from his suburb of St Alban to the Seevogelstrassse to show it to Overbeck. He knew that Overbeck had long been a good friend of Nietzsche's and knew also that there was a constant correspondence between them. He handed the letter to Overbeck who knew immediately that something was amiss. More than anything he was astonished that Nietzsche should have written such a letter to Burckhardt and the fact that he was now there standing at the front door for the first time meant as much to him as the letter which had been placed in his hand. Overbeck at once sat down and wrote a quick letter to Turin asking Nietzsche to come immediately to his house in Basle but this letter was crossed by another from the desk in Turin, 'I still hope to show that I am one who pays his debts, for example, to you. I have just had all anti-semites shot'. Again, it was signed 'Dionysus'.

This second letter convinced Overbeck that he could wait no longer. He made his way at once to Wille, a well known Basle psychiatrist and showed him both his own letter and the one to Burckhardt. Wille read the letters and suggested that Overbeck get Nietzsche to his clinic if it were at all possible. He impressed on Overbeck the need to get to Turin before anything irrevocable happened and that it might help to send a wire on ahead to let Nietzsche know that he was on his way. This was done immediately and, on the same evening, Overbeck caught the train for Turin. He arrived in the nick of time. As he approached the door of Davide Fino's house on the following afternoon, he met the landlord leaving on his way

DAVID POLLARD

to call the police and request the help of the German consul. The lodgings were in chaos. Nietzsche had again being singing and playing the piano and generally driving everyone to the point of desperation. When Overbeck entered the room he found Nietzsche crouched in a corner studying the proofs of his 'Nietzsche contra Wagner'. When he saw Overbeck he dropped the pages and, beginning to weep, struggled over to embrace him. He was in a terrible state and fell back onto the couch shaking from head to foot as if the greeting had half destroyed him. Fino's wife succeeded in giving him a phial of bromide and he calmed down enough to begin telling them of the ceremonies and pageants which had been prepared for his new dignity. He accompanied himself on the piano in muffled and mystical chords as he sang bits and pieces of his latest ideas and talked about his new existence as successor of the dead divinities of the world's history. Then, as he paused and pondered for a moment, another Nietzsche emerged, the jester who danced about the room making scurrilous jokes. Overbeck despaired of getting his friend all the way to Basle in this state.

But then he had a piece of luck. He was told of a German dentist called Miescher who had had some experience in escorting mental patients and was prepared to help for a small fee. Overbeck was very glad to take advantage of the man and they set off. The journey started out well enough but soon turned into an epic. There were a thousand difficulties. An incident in the streets of Turin might have brought in the Italian authorities and result in a refusal to allow Nietzsche to leave the country. Such problems could easily have occurred in the crowded streets or in the railway station where they had to wait for over half an hour in the middle of the afternoon or at Novarra where there was another enforced wait of three hours. But in the end everything went well, largely due to Miescher's acumen and experience. When his patient refused to leave his room Miescher told him that he had to visit Basle because of the great pageants and festivities that had been arranged there in his honour and when he stopped in the middle

135

of the street and began to make a speech to the crowds Miescher persuaded him that he wasn't behaving like a great and influential person who is obliged to remain incognito in public places. For most of the journey itself Nietzsche slept after being given a draught of chloral. Once he woke up as the train was steaming through the night over the St Gothard pass and began to sing a wonderful song with a strange and beautiful melody. It was his last poem, 'The Venetian Gondola', in which he tells of his soul singing a song tremulous with rich joy but which ends 'Was anyone listening?' The three of them arrived at Basle station at a quarter to eight the following morning, Thursday 10th of January. Nietzsche walked calmly from the train to a waiting cab and sat silently huddled in the corner during the whole of the long journey to the nursing home at Friedmatt where Wille ushered them all into the waiting room. Overbeck was terrified of this meeting because Nietzsche had known Wille back in his days at the University of Basle and, should he recognise him as head of the asylum, would know immediately where he was. He need not have worried for Nietzsche failed to recognise Wille. Instead he waited until Wille had left the room and asked politely why he had not been introduced. Another crisis had passed but Overbeck was still afraid that any mention of Wille's name would stir up memories for his friend and he kept silent. Nietzsche waited until Wille re-entered the room, went up to him and said in his politest manner, 'I am sure I have seen you before, and profoundly sorry but I cannot remember your name. I wonder if you would be so kind?' Overbeck held his breath while Wille introduced himself and was relieved to see that Nietzsche showed no sign of recognition but continued, 'Wille? ah yes you are an alienist. Some years ago we had a conversation about religious mania, the subject of our discussion was a madman called Adolph Vischer who was staying here'. Overbeck recalled the meeting well and was astonished at the fact the Nietzsche could remember it in such detail. Wille nodded in agreement but Nietzsche did not seem to relate his earlier visit to this alienist as

136

relevant to his presence in the clinic and allowed himself to be lead out of the room by one of Wille's assistants.

Wille decided that Nietzsche should be put into his private nursing home immediately. Only then did Overbeck feel that it was safe for him to leave.

The Clinical records speak of Nietzsche as follows 'The patient arrived accompanied by Professor Overbeck and Herr Miescher. He offered no resistance when he was led off. On the way he said that he regretted we were having such bad weather and added, I would prepare the loveliest weather for you good people tomorrow. He ate his breakfast ravenously. He also enjoyed his bath. He was in every way obedient and obliging. The patient gave no trouble while he was being examined and talked the whole time. He did not seem to be conscious of his illness but rather felt exceptionally well and exalted. He said that he had been ill for the previous week and often suffered from severe headaches, that he had had a few attacks and that while they were on he felt exceptionally well and that he would have liked to have embraced and kissed everyone in the street and would even have liked to have climbed up the walls. It was difficult to keep the patient's concentration on any one definite thing. He gave only fragmentary and imperfect answers or none at all. The patient stayed in bed the whole day. He had an excellent appetite and was very grateful for everything that was given him. In the afternoons he kept up a continual confused talk, breaking occasionally into singing and shouting. The content of his conversation was a jumble of previous experiences and thoughts followed each other without any logical connection. He stated that he had infected himself on two specific occasions'.

11th January 1889, 'The patient did not manage to sleep at all during the night and talked without a break.

137

He got up on several occasions to brush his teeth and wash himself. Overtired in the morning. Ate his breakfast hungrily and then remained in bed until noon. In the afternoon he went out but was in a continual state of excitement. Sometimes he threw his hat on the ground and even lay down on the ground himself. He spoke confusedly and occasionally reproached himself with having caused the ruin of several people'.

12th January, 'Was given sulfonal and got four or five hours sleep but with frequent interruptions. Was quieter in the morning. When he was asked how he felt he answered that he felt so incredibly well that he would only be able to express it in music'.

13th January, 'Slept better - six or seven hours. Patient had an enormous appetite and kept on asking for more food. In the afternoon he went for a walk in the garden. He sang, whimpered and shouted. Sometimes he took off his coat and waistcoat and lay down on the ground. After the walk he stayed in this room'.

14th January, 'Managed to sleep for four or five hours but when awake he talked and sang continually. He was expecting a visit from his mother today'.

Wille's diagnosis was paralysis progressiva. Overbeck now wrote to Nietzsche's mother and she arrived at the clinic on 13th January with the one fixed idea of getting her son back to Naumberg where she could care for him herself. She was ushered into Nietzsche's room where there was an emotional scene. Immediately on seeing her he embraced her warmly and said, 'My dear good mama, I am so very glad to see you'. The two of them then sat down and reminisced about the family for some time during which Wille looked on with astonishment. In the middle of this discussion Nietzsche suddenly jumped up and shouted, 'Behold in me the tyrant of Turin'. After which the conversation deteriorated into confusion and the visit was quietly ended. His mother was not frightened by this outburst and tried to persuade everyone to let her take him back to Naumberg with her but she was overruled.

Three days later Nietzsche was taken to a clinic nearer to Naumberg where he could be visited by his mother more easily. Her entreaties to have him with her in the house at Naumberg itself were defeated by the concerns of the medical men who were worried by his inclination to violence but they did finally agree to have him moved to Jena and stay at the clinic there run by Dr Binswanger.

The records of the final three days of Nietzsche's stay at Basle are as follows

15th January, 'Slept between four and five hours during the night but was noisy for the remainder of the time. Settled down during the afternoon. Patient drank a great deal of water. During his afternoon walk in the garden he strolled about gesticulating and shouting. Bath with cold water in the evening. Sulfinal 2.0. '

16th January, no entry.

17th January, 'Slept very well last night and was calmer early in the day. Paresis of the left facial muscle was much more noticeable than during the last few days but there is no obvious disturbance in his speech. He is going to be transferred to the asylum at Jena this evening. Weight 10th January 65 Kilos. 17th January 65.5 Kilos'.

The insistence of his mother finally overruled all objections and that evening Nietzsche left the clinic at Basle against the judgement of both Overbeck and Wille. With his mother went a doctor and another helper. They reached the Central Station of Basle early in the evening and Nietzsche got down from the cab and walked in absolute silence across the brightly lit station with rapid uncertain steps. He looked unnaturally stiff and his face was like a mask. They took him to a compartment which had been reserved and the small party settled in. Just as the train was about to leave, Overbeck, who had done so much for his friend over the previous few days, came to say good-bye. Nietzsche recognised him in the gloom of the compartment, got up from his seat and embraced him. As he did so he told Overbeck that 'he was the man he had loved most of all'. Overbeck was overcome with grief as he watched the train pull slowly out of the station, guilty that he left his friend in other hands but sad, too, that this was no longer his friend but another man, a mask, a mystery. Later Overbeck, thinking back on those few days, wondered whether he had done the right thing in drawing Nietzsche into the realm of doctors, asylums and medication. Were these, he now wondered, the actions of a true friend? He wrote to Gast that 'it would have been a far more genuine act of real friendship to have taken his life. Now, I have no other wish than that he should have his life taken from him and feel no hesitation at all in saying so. No-one who had been with me over these last days would wish it otherwise. It is all over with Friedrich! I do not need any reports from doctors to confirm that all hope of a cure is out of the question. Judge of this yourself by one point only. Friedrich can not even hate me now for the one thing of which I am most guilty, the sin of robbing him of his freedom. This is the tragedy of this hero of freedom - he no longer thinks of freedom'.

The journey started off well enough. Mother and son seemed happy to be together after their long separation. She handed him some sandwiches and he commented on how nice they were. When she gave him some cherries he said, 'I suppose that you have brought these all the way from the Cherry Fair at Naumberg'. He seemed perfectly well, better than the attendant who had been with him at

Basle had yet seen him. He told his mother that he had been in a bad way and had been taken to a lunatic asylum but that he would soon be well again because, after all, he was still young, a mere twenty-two. However, the doctor's fears finally proved well founded and the thing they most feared soon happened. Nietzsche flew into a rage against his mother. Although it only lasted a minute or two it was a dreadful thing for her to have to see and she quickly moved to another compartment and left him to the doctors until they arrived at Frankfort.

On the Friday, 18th January, Nietzsche was admitted to the Mental Home of the Grand Duchy of Sachsen Weimar at Jena. On admission he walked through the building with majestic strides and a great deal of polite bowing. He thanked everyone for the magnificent reception he had been given. He seemed to have no idea where he was. At one moment he imagined himself to be in Naumberg and at another he spoke as if he were in Turin. He constantly offered to shake the doctors' hands. But all the personal information which he provided was accurate. To look at he seemed self-assured. He gesticulated a lot and spoke continuously even during the nights and in a rather affected voice, sometimes in Italian and sometimes in French. He didn't speak German to these Germans. But what he said was somewhat disconnected. He spoke of his grand compositions and insisted in singing some of them as a demonstration. He told them of his many councillors and servants.

His mother was told that she must keep away from the clinic for the time being as the aim was to try to calm the patient down. She agreed finally and returned home. The treatment, however, did not immediately succeed.

On his arrival at Jena we have

1. Behaviour: On admission brought here by his mother and a Basle doctor from the Basle Mental Clinic where he

141

had stayed for several days after he was fetched from Turin. Record of his illness from Basle; Bath. Put to bed. Medium build.

2. Heredity: Father died of softening of the brain - Some of father's, brothers and sisters suffering from rickets, very talented. Mother living, untalented. Brothers and sisters 1, Friedrich, 2. Elizabeth, living married to Bernhard Förster, in good health. 3, Joseph, deceased, stroke at age of 2.

3. Life history: Always rather peculiar. Very gifted. Pupil of Ritschl. On his recommendation Professor at Basle at age of 23. 1866. Suphilit. infect. 1869 appointed Professor of Classical Philology at Basle.

4. History of disease: 1878 Gave up professorship because of nervousness and eye trouble.

Over the next three days a more detailed examination was carried out. The notes read:

Present condition 19-21. 1.89. Large sized man (171 cm), fairly muscular, muscles moderately well covered. 132 lbs. Hair brown, somewhat sparse. Iris, brownish green. Right ear 5.8, left 5.6 long. Circumference of skull 57 cm, high arched pallet. Face very flushed. Heart sound low-pitched, normal. Vasomotor system normal. Arteries soft, tortuous. Lung apices normal. Tongue slightly furred. Pupils, right wide, left rather narrower, left contracted with slight irregularity, all reactions normal on left, on right only reaction to convergence, consensual reaction only on left. Considerable anophthalmia on left side, no secondary internal strabismus. Forehead wrinkled, eyes half closed symmetrically. Shows teeth more on left, right corner of mouth turned down somewhat, mouth closed more firmly on right. Symmetrical smile. Tongue non-tremulous with deviations to right. Uvula in midline, pressure of hand firmer on left than on right (specimens of handwriting).

Romberg sign negative. When walking, patient screws left shoulder up spasmodically leaving right shoulder down. Sways when turning right. Increased muscular irritability. Myodema. Anconaeus reflex slightly increased. Patellar reflex ditto. Ankle jerk ditto, slight ankle clonus on left, abdominal reflex slightly increased. Cremaster reflex weak on left. Plantar reflex increased. Condition of patient does not allow sensibility test at present. Apparently general hyperaesthesia. Head percussion not sensitive. Facial nerves sensitive. Pressure on body cannot be tested because of hyperaesthesia. Bone conduction apparently better on right. Hearing distance apparently intact left and right. No disturbance in reading. Considerable myopia. No defect of speech, rarely hesitates over initial consonants. Tactile discrimination normal.

After this the records read as follows,`

20th January, 'did not sleep despite being given amylene hydrate. Finally transferred to a ward which allowed for constant supervision'.

21st January, 'was noisy continually despite being given chloral and had finally to be isolated. Mentioned on one occasion that his father had suffered from softening of the brain'.

22nd January, 'insistent that one of his compositions be performed. Complained of headaches and thought that this was the reason that he was so lively'.

24th January, 'very noisy. Has had to be isolated once again'.

10th February, 'still very noisy. Regular outbursts of rage with inarticulate shouting for no apparent reason'.

The man who had so very carefully studied himself was now being very carefully studied by others.

The records continue in this way for some little while. The patient scrawled incomprehensibly on the walls of the clinic, continued with his fits of rage, smashed a

143

window. He spent a lot of time in bed, sometimes insisting that he needed a sleep in the middle of the day and refusing to get up again and still the grimacing and the shouting. He was being tortured during the night and there were attempts on his life. He demanded a revolver for protection.

Eventually a change occurred, he began to calm down and his mother was allowed in to see him from time to time in a separate room put aside for the purpose. Nietzsche was still exultant, 'Is this not a magnificent room. I give my lectures here in front of a select public'. While she was with him he found a pencil and, pleading for an envelope which he had seen his mother carrying, began to make notes on it. Before she left, she saw him take another pencil and gather together some pieces of paper that were lying around. She said as a joke, 'Dear Friedrich, you are becoming a thievish little mouse' and he whispered in her ear, 'Now I shall have something to do when I creep back into my cave'.

Nietzsche continued much the same. He began to understand that he was in an asylum and some of the more fixed notions which he had had earlier began to disappear. He tended to keep himself to himself. When he spoke it was usually in French and often about music. Sometimes he would pick up a newspaper and read it for a few moments but then would crumple it up and throw it on the floor. One particular patient he would watch with care. This was a musician who would spend his time writing down his compositions. One day Nietzsche smashed a window and cut himself. While the wound was being looked at in the asylum lending library he looked at some of the books with interest. When he was walking in the garden he drew geometric figures in the sand. Things improved, although there were still bad lapses which were considered dangerous. Little by little he was allowed to see more visitors, especially his mother. He was now more manageable and his helpers were discovering how to control him.

With his mother he behaved more and more like his earlier self. His appearance and carriage seemed to have been restored. He had a healthy look in his eyes and was cheerful. Only his talk was still strange, somewhat affected or regimental especially when he wanted to say something important. Of one of her visits she writes, 'He did not give a wrong opinion or use a wrong word for two hours or more although you do have to lead him in conversation'. They spoke about Förster and about his old school at Pforta and about Ritschl at Leipzig and his answers were all quite clear and based on a good recollection of his life. But finally he looked at her and then around at the asylum and said, 'When shall I get out of this place?' She assured him that she would get him away soon and he told her, 'I have had a lot of headaches and I have been ill a lot of my life and have often vomited as well'.

On 21st January Gast visited and saw him for the first time in over two years. He wrote of that meeting, 'He did not look too bad, I would almost like to say that his mental disturbance consists merely in an accentuation of the humorous side of his nature which he used to show to his friends. He knew me immediately, embraced and kissed me and was delighted to see me. He gave me his hand over and over again as if he could not believe that I was actually there'.

By the beginning of February 1890 he had become much more malleable. Gast wrote on the first of the month, 'Today I am enormously strengthened in my feeling that we shall have our Friedrich back again. Yesterday and today he was splendid!'

In the middle of the February his mother moved to a little flat which she had rented in Jena and began to get ready for the arrival of her son. She called at the clinic every day and stayed there from nine in the morning until after six in the evening. Gast was with her. Nietzsche was now childishly docile and soon he was allowed to spend part of each day in his mother's flat. Gast had rented the floor below so that he could be on call. Sometimes

145

he was needed. Once, after his mother had cleaned his spectacles, they fell of the ground and the lens fell out of its gold frame. Nietzsche began to cry. It was only when Gast came and fixed the lens back again that he calmed down.

On 24th February Overbeck arrived and, like Gast, was allowed to pass a lot of time with Nietzsche outside the asylum. He wrote, 'A third person, a perfect stranger who might have come upon us together, would have noticed hardly anything strange in Nietzsche's behaviour save for one or two oddities. At table or in the street he sometimes tried to hit dogs or even people who appeared suddenly'. But Nietzsche was now in his posthumous existence. Overbeck continues, 'Outwardly we were old friends and I alone knew that our association was now entirely based upon the past. Nietzsche greeted me at our first meeting in his mother's flat as though nothing had changed in our old friendship and so it remained until I left Jena. His loquacity increased during our conversations but these talks were based almost entirely on events which had occurred before his insanity. I often tried to direct his thoughts to more recent events but in vain because his responses were confused. He seemed to have no memory of his immediate past or of his life in the asylum. Indeed, he seemed at times to be avoiding it on purpose, as if this was something that was not available for speech. Our talks were restricted entirely to the past that lay behind that moment in Turin. It was as though we existed on two different planets, myself in an old and he in a new one. We could speak only of the old planet and then his memories of it came only in fragments. We spoke sometimes of his returning to teach at the University at Basle. He mentioned it often in the belief that he would soon re-enter that old world. But such fragments were always of the external events of his past. He never spoke of his internal life, of his writings or his thought. There were none of those moments of vision, of imagination, to which I had become accustomed. It was as if he had left all that behind and had calmed down to the point of depression or of weariness. There was no opposition to one's point of view, none of the old energy in argument. Merely agreement with everything that was said and an easy ability to be swayed from one subject to another. At the end of our walks he was easily led back into the asylum without the slightest difficulty'.

Gast left Jena at the beginning of March and he noted, 'When I went away there were tears in his eyes. He was particularly lucid on that day and the farewell touched me very much'. He added, 'to see this titan broken because his mental gifts were too strong for the physical frame which held them, to see the noblest of human beings broken and become a mockery of himself because in all things he was too divine, to see him an object of pity for those over whom he should wield his sceptre was terrible'.

An earlier hint, 'I too have been in the underworld like Odysseus and shall often be there again. I have not merely sacrificed sheep but have not spared even my own blood in order to converse with some of the dead. May the living forgive me if at times they seem to me as shadows'.

Footfalls - The Archive

End of 'Nueva Germania' and of queen-hood model one. Although Elizabeth had returned from Paraguay, disappointed and widowed, her need to create a New Germany and to be a part of it had not ended. Far from it. The little goblins still hovered around her neck and shoulders and demons played around her hair. The queen of 'Nueva Germania' now began to make herself queen of New Germany. It wasn't easy but she did it. Later, Cosima, furious at the success of her new rival, commented to her daughter, 'Did you know that Elizabeth Nietzsche is now living a life of luxury with servants and an equipage'. The Nietzsche cult was so successful that it was becoming a threat to the Wagner cult and that would never do.

But first the boss must make herself the boss. She moved the madman to her mother's house, 18 Weingarten, in Naumberg. Her mother was given the task of caring for the body while Elizabeth began to deal with the mind. She stuffed all the material she had already collected plus everything that she could lay her hands on in the downstairs rooms. The house was renamed 'The Nietzsche Archive'. It was graced with headed notepaper and opened on 2nd February 1894. She made a grab for everything, a process which she was well used to. From her earliest years she had begged, borrowed or stolen her brother's material, all the stuff which he would have burnt or thrown away, putting it carefully into boxes. Now she appointed herself as sole and official editor of all his material. The landlord of the house in Sils Maria had collected every bit of paper which Nietzsche had thrown into the wastepaper basket in his room. He had been happily giving them away piece by piece to anyone who bothered to ask even though Nietzsche had told him to destroy everything. Elizabeth wrote demanding it all back and got it. She soon expanded, grabbing for herself the rights to everything he had written, getting her mother to sign away her title as executrix, suing anyone who published anything which she felt was hers and sending requests to everyone she could think of to return letters sent to them by her brother. Most concurred. Cosima refused, burning the lot.

Peter Gast had been asked by Nietzsche's mother to edit a collected edition with his own introductions. However, he soon discovered Elizabeth's intentions. He had been at work on the texts for a year when she re-appeared. He wrote to Overbeck, 'An event has occurred that is bound to disrupt both myself and the whole Nietzsche cause. Frau Förster has returned from Paraguay. There followed a couple of days during which I was tempted to chuck in my editorship'. No need. He was sacked as soon as convenient.

She discovered quickly that her brother's work was valuable. She began to publish cheap editions and settled down to write a biography, resolving that she would be the only channel to her brother's philosophy, 'I, more than anyone, am duty bound to repulse attacks, to remove mistakes and portray the facts and experiences of my brother's life with the most precise accuracy as no-one stood as close to him as I did'. Of course, she had a problem. Much of her brother's thought was anathema to her and could never be allowed to see the light of day. All that, she simply discarded. In her efforts to create the image she desired, she chose to ignore those elements in his philosophy with which she couldn't agree. Then there was another problem, even closer to her heart. The relationship between Nietzsche and herself. Obviously she wanted to show this in the best possible light. This was not so easy or, if you like, was very easy indeed. The big lie is always the easiest lie as Goebbels knew so well. Thus, when she came across letters which contained compliments addressed to others, she would singe their names away with a candle and claim that they has been sent to her. She became a forger on a truly grand scale.

How do we know that this happened? Well, some of those correspondents had kept copies of their letters and didn't like praise which had been directed at them being hijacked by a third party.

The task she had set herself was an imposing one so she gathered malleable and subservient editorial help around her. Gast, the only man then alive capable of deciphering Nietzsche's appalling scrawl, had already prepared an edition before he had been sacked. He was replaced by Dr Fritz Koegel. Another useful follower was Rudolph Steiner, later to found anthroposophy, who agreed to instruct Elizabeth in the fundamentals of her brother's thought. The job proved difficult, 'Frau Nietzsche [...] lacks all sense of fine and even of crude logical distinctions. Her thinking is void of even the smallest logical consistency. [...] She can persuade herself that what was blue yesterday is red today'. Thus the luck of the draw for editors.

On her mother's death she took her brother to Weimar, seat of German learning and home of Liszt, Goethe and Schiller. Here, she thought, he would be in the right sort of company. With money given by Meta von Salis, she bought the Villa Silberblick. The fact that it was an impressive edifice constructed on high ground must have allowed her to ignore its name which, as well as 'silvern view', also means 'squint', a problem that Elizabeth had always suffered from. She would disturb people by seeming to look at something away in the distance a little over their left shoulder. Her philosophical and political squints were no less disconcerting. She ripped the place to pieces and turned it into a shrine to herself and all her associations, to the memories of her brother and her husband. It was done up in pink and made to look like a funeral parlour. It had a bust of Nietzsche at one end and one of Förster at the other. A huge 'N' (with vague echoes of an earlier dictator with large ambitions) was embossed in brass over the fireplace. Thus Walter Jessinghaus, 'From Kaiserin Augusta Strasse which curves down from Wieland Square into Louisen Strasse and along it to number 30. This is beyond the town, past the Felsenkeller inn. The villa lies in its own grounds commanding a view of its surroundings'. Philo van Walden tells us, 'The house has three floors and a mansard apartment'. The style is simple, plain but noble, 'an un-stuccoed red-brick building with white trim, a gently sloping slate roof, lobby and balcony, a large garden with young olive trees and clusters of other trees all around'. It is a 'beautiful home which overlooks the meadows far and wide'. There is 'a splendid view over the whole city and beyond to the sumptuous crops and the green forests that covered the hilly landscape on the other side'. Van Walden again, 'Peaceful solitude, distant horizons, laughing sky all around and golden sunshine in all the windows'.

Today the building is still there. A short gravel drive leads up to the front door above which is a grey stone block on which is a chiselled inscription, 'Nietzsche Archiv'. Inside is a photograph of the place during Elizabeth's reign. The inscription then was a little different. It read, 'Nietzsche Archiv. In memory. Placed here by Adolf Hitler in the sixth year of the Third Reich'. The building has survived the war intact on top if its hill and stands there today overlooking the countryside to the west; square, solid and quite imposing in its quiet middle-brow way. Inside it is not difficult to imagine it as it was although there have been some changes. The bust of Förster has gone. The room in which Nietzsche lived those three years and in which he died is occupied by a student and the staircase to the upper floors is roped off. Let's hope that whoever sleeps there now has pleasant dreams.

Elizabeth set to work with a will. Jessinghaus again, 'It is known at least in her circle of friends with what indust-

151

riousness and endurance she often works late into the night in the interest of her brother's great cause. When everyone far and wide is already fast asleep, her lamp - the only light in all that darkness - is still shining in the window of her room and keeps company with the restlessly active woman who in spite of the hard heavy suffering inflicted on her by fate, still looks insistently and actively into life and reveals no trace of brooding pessimism'.

Guests were overawed at Elizabeth's staging of her brother. Occasionally they were even allowed into his presence. Dr Horneffer in August 1899, 'Anyone who has seen Nietzsche as a patient must consider himself lucky [...] How impressed I was by his beauty! Nietzsche lay on a sofa wrapped in a loose white cloak - I always saw him only in this cloak which heightened his prophetic appearance - and the impression was powerful, indeed overpowering [...] a prophet of divine simplicity, nothing fancy in his being, in a word the Zarathustra Nietzsche. I stood still, awe-struck with reverence [...] There was something of Goethe, Jupiter-like [...] Nietzsche emanated a sovereignty that seemed to force the world to its knees'.

So many deaths which are not really deaths, of men who go on living even though the clocks have stopped, who live through a time that is static and eternal, through a temporal silence which no pulse punctures.

History enforces other time scales which rip through our spatial certainties, twisting them askew and dropping them in unexpected places. The smallest shift can do it, even a shift as small and as insignificant as death in which so little changes. In that war in which the dictator fought as a corporal 'Every soldier killed in action died with his knapsack on. When he fell he displaced nothing; his belt, his cartridge boxes, his tassel, bayonet and spade, tent square, the rolled up greatcoat [...] everything in its proper place, folded up and buttoned and tied fast [...] not even the helmet and its cover rolled away or came off the head. It was as if he had prepared himself for a parade of the dead'. And in his knapsack was Elizabeth's edition of 'Thus Spake Zarathustra'. Or a different experience encountered unexpectedly like the soldier in one of those innumerable winter trenches dug into a frozen landscape who wrote later that 'A shell missed me outside Albert and did for my watch. I could shake it, and it would tick for a bit, but the spring was gone. I've an idea I don't grow any older now'. 'Suddenly somewhere a little thing slips, some little tiny thing. Gliss-iss-iss STOP! I trust I make myself clear'. Tales of the living dead, of zombies not left to lie in peaceful graves but who rise from the tomb and stalk the world in posthumous existences.

Footfalls are heard padding across the floor of the room above while the sister struggles on with her task of editing and re-writing, struggles on into the night. Even makes him famous and popular. Her indomitable will is in step with the times and her brother's thought has a line put through it here and a scratched improvement there... And, like his works, his body is also edited quite out of its own reality. Sometimes he is helped to the veranda and sits there watching the sun drop ever so slowly behind the Etersburg hills. Maybe he felt like the poet Keats writing from his room overlooking the Piazza di Spagna, 'I have a habitual feeling of my real life having past, and that I am leading a posthumous existence'. 'God knows, 'he added, 'how it would have been'. His star predominant. There are so many different types of murder and the quick knife in the dark may be the kindest. But a murder of ten years!

In August 1900, at the age of 55, Nietzsche finally died. Elizabeth sent out cards, 'At around twelve o'clock today my dearly-beloved brother Friedrich Nietzsche passed away. Weimar 25th August 1900. Elizabeth Förster-Nietzsche'. Another, 'The burial will take place on Tuesday 28th August at 4 o'clock in the afternoon in the family plot at Röcken in the state of Lützen'.

In his writing he had pronounced an intense curse on Christianity and all religion. The aims of Christianity are 'the poisoning, slandering, life denying, contempt for the body, the denigration and self violation of man via the concept of sin. As a consequence its means are also bad'. Again, 'Its essence is a sickness'. And again and again. 'God is dead and we have killed him. There has never been a greater deed'. He had asked his sister as she herself tells it, 'Lisbeth, my brother said solemnly, when I die promise me that only friends will stand around the coffin - no inquisitive crowd, Make sure that no priest nor anyone else will pronounce falsehoods at my graveside when I can no longer defend myself and let me be lowered into my grave as sincere pagan'. Elizabeth ignored this plea and he was buried with all the rites of the Lutheran church, in a coffin adorned with a silver crucifix. Peter Gast read the words over the coffin, 'Hallowed be thy name to all future generations'. Nietzsche had earlier written, 'I have a terrible fear that one day I shall be pronounced holy. I do not want to be a saint'.

His grave is now in the churchyard at Röcken parsonage where he lies to the left of his sister. Or, at least somewhat to the left, and maybe just a little under his sister. His is the only grave with flowers. His death mask is ... archaeological, unreal. Done in white plaster, it looks slightly cracked and broken and perhaps this is appropriate. She allowed none of him to escape.

Not excluding his moustache. Nietzsche's moustache, so the story goes, was neatly severed from his body while it lay in its coffin and offered for sale to a number of institutions including some renowned German universities all of which solemnly refused it. Its whereabouts are now unkown.

By then, her biography of Nietzsche was finished. It was in three volumes and became very popular. Really little more than a piece of hagiography, it was full of inaccuracies and lies which were designed to recreate him as a prophet and show how close he had been to his sister. She wrote, 'Never in our lives did we say an unkind word to each other'. Max Heinze accurately summarised her efforts as 'the erection of a splendid memorial to yourself as his sister'. Von Seydlitz agreed, 'You have erected a heroic monument to himself and yourself'.

Then there is the question of the final work, 'The Will to Power', the book that Bäumler called 'Nietzsche's philosophical magnum opus'. The kleptomaniac publishes the results of her crimes, not so much a forgery as a piece of alchemy. Under the name of Friedrich Nietzsche comes a collection of discarded notes, unfinished aphorisms and other scraps which Nietzsche had never collected together as a book. Here were all the scribbles and notes which he had put down on paper between 1883 and 1888 and rejected. But Elizabeth turned this material into the final statement of the Nietzschian philosophy, a summing up of his thinking over all of his creative life. These bits and pieces she put in her own order, arranging them under four headings, an order which had been superceeded by some 25 later drafts. The implication was that he had finally come round to promoting breeding, discipline and the priority of Germany, in other words almost everything that he spent his life labouring against.

The old difficult struggling plant had withered in the wrong kind of soil but this new hybrid flourished. Under Elizabeth's careful nurturing Nietzsche rapidly grew into a household name. When the congress of the International Psychoanalytic Association came to town they avoided the archive on the hill even though it was mentioned

155

often enough that Nietzsche had anticipated many of it's findings. Elizabeth knew well enough that her old enemy Lou von Salomé was one of the leading lights of this new movement and must have been furious at the thought that her brother's name was being associated with it, led as it was by that Jew Freud. But she had to keep her infuriation under wraps.

This however, was a mere blip in her resolute progress. She was a good populist and had an understanding of marketing methods which Goebbels might later have secretly applauded. Horrified when Lou Salomé had published articles and even a book on Nietzsche, she had angrily called it 'exploitation' but didn't balk at doing the same herself. She published cheap editions of her brother's works and they sold well. By the First World War she was already well known as his executor. That war presented her with no twinge of a moral choice. Nietzsche was an imperialist and warmonger and, of course, would have been in favour of the cause.

Elizabeth paid for copies of her edition of 'Thus Spoke Zarathustra' to be put into every soldier's knapsack and, from the sidelines, she encouraged those same soldiers into battle, 'This is a great challenge to Germans to rise up and fight. There is a fighter in every German no matter which party he belongs to and this warrior comes to the fore whenever the fatherland is threatened'. Closer reading of Nietzsche would have found, 'Germans have no idea of how vile they are'. There is even the hope that, 'Perhaps there will come in the future a great day on which a nation distinguished for war and victory of its own volition will declare: "we will smash the sword and demolish our entire military machine down to the last foundations"'.

When faced with the reality of defeat Elizabeth was devastated and ranted, 'I cannot stand it. At the front our armies were undefeated but our stupid home guards, fools and children, have stabbed our brave soldiers in the back. Germany offers a dreadful spectacle. Every day I wish that I were dead'.

But that was mere hyperbole. She didn't die. Instead she redoubled her propaganda programme. She was becoming very successful at it. Money was no longer a problem as her publishing activities were bringing in real cash flow. She could afford an extravagant lifestyle. She was even put up for the Nobel prize for literature and, although she was refused the honour three times in a row, she did get an honorary doctorate and was on her way to being Germany's first woman of letters. She was accepted as the official broker of her brother's thought. The Nietzsche Archive had its queen bee surrounded by a creative hive of servants, secretaries, lawyers and editors. Weimar was also becoming a social centre.

Since the death of her husband, Elisabeth had remained a widow. Nietzsche's death had made her a kind of double widow and she always dressed the part. Never seen in anything other than long, black dresses with plenty of lace and tulle at the neck and wrists. She usually topped the ensemble off with a little black hat. By the 1930s her clothes had become a little more ample and the hats rather larger and she had taken to sporting a small umbrella when out of doors. She looked a little like Queen Victoria, the severe widow in perpetual mourning. But in Elizabeth's case the resignation which this persona implies was missing. Her aim was to make Weimar the intellectual capital of Germany and add the name of Nietzsche to those of Goethe and Schiller.

To this end she grabbed at every possible opportunity and it was an Italian one that now swam into view. Unlike Hitler, it is quite possible that Mussolini had actually read some Nietzsche. But he followed the sister rather than the brother, quoting out of context and managing to make Nietzsche support his own thinking. Mussolini thought of Nietzsche as his one key influence. He saw himself as a superman who could transcend social norms and grab

157

directly at what he wanted. Elizabeth was thrilled to be shown an article in the papers reporting that Mussolini admired her brother. Her response was immediate. She ordered Max Oehler to produce an article in reply showing how Mussolini was the fulfilment of Nietzsche's social theories. The article was published in both the German and Italian press and was read by Mussolini.

In this way, by the middle of the 1920s, she had begun to open up direct lines of contact with Italian fascism. Her 'New Caesar' marched on Rome and took power in a coup d'état in 1922. Elizabeth was delighted, 'I can no longer restrain myself from expressing my admiration. He is not only the pre-eminent statesman of Europe but of the whole world. With what pride my brother would have gazed on this wonderful man, on someone happy, powerful and triumphant, who offers mankind the hope of salvation'. She saw Mussolini as the living embodiment of her brother's philosophy and her thrilled expression of the fact brought its response. A constant flood of encouragement came from Italy in the form of letters, telegrams and money. Elizabeth's probing uncovered the fact that Mussolini had written a play and, in February 1932, she arranged a production of it at Weimar's National Theatre sending a fulsome letter to Mussolini imploring him to come to Germany for the first night. Mussolini replied equally fulsomely that unfortunately he was not able etc. However, in the event, Elizabeth was not to be disappointed, for, that night, she met another and even more pre-eminent statesman of the whole world, Adolf Hitler, who entered the theatre surrounded by his storm troopers, made straight for Elizabeth's private box and presented her with a large bunch of roses in front of a rapturous first night audience. Elizabeth remembered, 'His eyes are fascinating. They look right through you'. She might not have realised it at the time but she had finally met the man who would give her the authority she had always craved. These two were quite happy to use each other to further their own ends. With the best will in the world.

When Hitler took power soon after, Elizabeth could hardly contain herself, 'We are drunk with enthusiasm because at the head of our government stands such a wonderful, indeed phenomenal, personality - our chancellor, Adolf Hitler. We have suddenly achieved the one Germany which for centuries our poets have longingly depicted in their poems and for which we have all being waiting. Ein Volk, Ein Reich. Ein Führer'. Just as Nietzsche had feared, "German" had become an argument, "Deutschland, Deutschland uber alles" had become 'a principle and the end of German thought'.

Much later in 1943 after the fall of southern Italy, Mussolini was deposed and put under house arrest well out of sight. From the ruler who had certainly never read any Nietzsche to the other one who certainly had was sent a copy of the collected works as a gift on his, the Italian one's, sixtieth birthday.

But Weimar was not the only pull on Hitler's cultural passions. There was also Bayreuth and the other story. Wagner also shared with the chancellor a passionate anti-semitism and it was almost inevitable that Bayreuth would become a centre for Nazi propaganda. Winifred Williams, a Welsh girl who became Wagner's daughter-in-law, was another keen Nazi. By 1924 Hitler had discovered Bayreuth. Siegfried Wagner noted that 'it was during this summer that we got to know this delightful man and we will not disappoint him even if we end up in prison (which, unlike so many, she didn't). In Bayreuth we have never made a secret of our ideas, Jew and Jesuit go hand in hand and seek to destroy what is essentially German'. There is a film made by Syberberg in 1976 for the cente- 159 nary of Bayreuth which shows Winifred Wagner talking about her great friend Adolf. She told the camera, 'He played the piano nicely. In his youth he composed an opera. He loved the children and treated the women with the greatest politeness [...] He hated discussing politics and talked passionately about stage problems. He had a deep love for, and knowledge of, Wagner's music which he tried to hear regularly despite the problems of his profession'. When he telephoned he always called himself Kapellmeister Wolf. When Winifred asked him why he liked the name Wolf he tells her, amazingly, 'Because it sounds so delightfully Jewish'.

Weimar and Bayreuth were soon the twin capitals of cultural Nazism, a connection which Elizabeth understood very well. She never accepted her brother's radical break with Wagner and his music, 'Those who understand my brother can see clearly how greatly he still admired Wagner as the most brilliant and impressive example of the modern soul'.

Elizabeth and Winifred were two pebbles from the same beach. Beyreuth now gloried in the full force of the Nazi propaganda machine. Elizabeth was also ravished, 'It was in the theatre during a performance in honour of the 30th anniversary of Wagner's death that I had the great good fortune of a personal conversation with our wonderful chancellor'. Weimar was becoming a setting for love affairs of this kind. Elizabeth had met Förster there half a century earlier and fallen for him. Now she was falling much more deeply for Hitler. Both, of course, marriages of devotion and convenience. Here the intricate webs began to get entangled and stirred into their inappropriate afterlives where two resurrections intermingle.

Hitler thought of himself as a man of letters, a philosopher king. Plato's philosopher king writes, 'We must not only compel our poets, on pain of expulsion (merely?) to make their poetry the express images of a noble character, we much also supervise craftsmen of every kind and forbid them to leave the stamp of baseness, license, meanness, unseemliness on painting and sculpture, on building or any other work of their hands and anyone who cannot obey shall not practice his art [...] we would not have our Guardians grow up amongst representations of moral deformity as in some foul pasture where [...] they would gather a mass of corruption in their very souls'. Thus Plato, thinking of Wagner and the Third Reich. And he continues, 'rather we must seek out those craftsmen and ....'

Hitler was, at the same time, politician, artist, architect and thinker and therefore the ideal man to dictate the basis of the art of his time. He roared, 'When does man live by bread alone? We have before us not only a suffering workforce but also an ample and struggling culture. Not only the needs of the body but also the needs of the soul. We cannot think of the German people rising again if German culture does not also rise'. Nietzsche had understood exactly the position which Germany had now reached and he had himself ranted against such rantings, 'Culture and the state - one should not deceive oneself in this - are antagonists. The one thrives at the expense of the other'. Thus the rise of the 'Reich' signifies one thing above all, 'a displacement of the centre of gravity away from Germany'. These warnings, however, Elizabeth managed to avoid. By now the Jewish Wagner conductors, Elmendorff and Muck, had been replaced by the Aryan Toscanini of whom Magee has written that, 'The most knowledgeable Wagnerians I know of, from Ernest Newman down, have tended to agree that the best performances they have ever heard were those of Toscanini in Bayreuth'. He, however, eventually left in disgust to be replaced by the politically more reliable Richard Strauss for whom, as Stephan Sweig wrote, 'It was of vital interest to be particularly co-operative with the National Socialists because [..] he was very much in the red with them. His son had married a Jewess and thus he feared that his grand-children [...] would be excluded from school as scum. His new opera was tainted through Sweig, his earlier opera through the half-Jew Hofmannsthal. His publisher was a Jew. Therefore it seemed to him increasingly impe-

161

rative to create some support and security for himself and he did it with great perseverance'. Like so many others he simply didn't see what was going on around him even though he had the ear of the führer and of most of the National Socialist bigwigs'. Roth could write that 'Strauss's complete detachment from all political and national affairs was truly monumental. It was no aversion, for any such aversion springs from an act of judgement. Politics simply has no entry whatever into his world'.

Toscanini escaped to Palestine at the invitation of Albert Einstein who called him 'a man who has shown the greatest dignity in the fight against the fascist criminals'. He stayed in Jerusalem for a month to help the newly created Palestinian Orchestra. He travelled. At almost seventy years of age he chased around the place going to Bethlehem and Nazareth, the Dead Sea, visiting a kibbutz and showing up at a Passover meal which was translated for him. His concerts, of which he gave three in Tel Aviv, three in Haifa and three in Jerusalem, were all sold out. He was enormously popular wherever he went, crowds lining the streets to catch a glimpse of him. A mother who gave birth to twins called them 'Tosca' and 'Nini'.

Interesting that, some thirty years earlier, in 1889 Nietzsche went to see a production of Carmen at the Teatro Carignano in Turin under the baton of Leopoldo Mugnono, the very production which was conducted the following year by Toscanini.

Hitler perfectly understood the propaganda value of both Bayreuth and the Nietzsche Archive. He saw, without ever reading a word of it, that Nietzsche's thought as propagated by his sister would give him some of the intellectual weight that he lacked. He nurtured Elizabeth and regularly visited her at Weimar. All of this was perfect for her master plan, 'If my brother had ever met him his greatest wish would have been fulfilled. He will change Germany completely. What I like most about Hitler is his simplicity' and, 'He wants nothing for himself but only for Germany. I admire him utterly'.

Nietzsche was grabbed by Nazism with open arms and given a hug so tight that it almost killed his reputation. He was at the core of their cultural mission. But that doesn't mean that they neglected other areas. Indeed not. Nazi propaganda reached its fingers into every corner of the national pie. Hitler, with Goebbels at his side, realised that culture was a central part of their political task. Decadence had to be destroyed and true German culture lauded. Philosophy and history, literature and religion were co-opted for the battle, 'In the one hand the book and in the other the sword - this is how our people have risen to their national transformation. It has advanced wonderfully before our very eyes. Book and sword are and remain the symbols of our time and are the decisive signs of the new century'. Any book thought decadent was burnt in a literary holocaust. May 10th 1933 saw a spectacle that had not been seen in Europe since the middle ages. A torch-light march of students in their thousands made its way to the Unter den Linden opposite the University of Berlin where a bonfire was built. Books were then thrown into the flames and some 20,000 volumes burnt to ashes, 'I consign to the flames the writings of Karl Marx and Leon Trotsky. I consign to the flames Heinrich Mann and Thomas Mann, Albert Einstein and Erich Kästner. I consign to the flames Sigmund Freud, Erich Maria Remarque, Andre Gide, Emile Zola and Marcel Proust'. Goebbels stood by the fire, 'For German men and women the time for decadent Jewish intellectualism is over. Our German revelation sets us free [...] The soul of the German people can again express itself. These flames not only illuminate the final end of an old era; they also light up the new'. While this was going on the work of Nietzsche, as radical as any that were being destroyed, became one of the

163

bibles of Nazism. In that bible are the words, 'Wherever Germany penetrates, she ruins culture'.

Eventually and inevitably the anti-semitism that the Nazis had been so assiduously encouraging erupted in the Krystallnacht. Jews were beaten up and their shops looted. Nietzsche was used to give intellectual backing to this thuggery. The man who had vigorously opposed anti-semitism was quoted to support Hitler's most savage decrees. Wrote Elizabeth, 'The link between Nietzsche and National Socialism is the heroism in both their souls'.

Nietzsche's attitude to the Germans becomes clearer as he goes along

'If ever my biography comes to be written, this statement should be put in, 'only among Germans was he treated badly'.

'Perhaps I understand the Germans, perhaps I can even presume to tell them a few home truths. The new Germany represents a plentiful amount of efficiency, inherited and acquired, so that for some time to come it even has a right to be extravagant in spending from the store of its accumulated energy. It is not a high culture that has gained the upper hand in Germany, still less a refined taste, a noble instinct for 'beauty' but virtues that are more manly than any other country in Europe can show an ample share of courage and self-respect, sterling honesty in the relations of life, a high sense of duty, great industry, great stamina - a hereditary temperance which needs the spur rather than the drag. I must add that here men obey without feeling humiliated by obedience [...] And no one despises his opponent'... .

But Nietzsche also wants to be just to the Germans to 'tell them what he objects to'.

Coming to power is costly, 'power makes stupid. The

Germans were once called the nation of thinkers. Do they still think at all? Nowadays the Germans are bored with in-tel-lect. Politics devours all serious things. 'Deutschland, Deutschland uber alles' was, I fear, the end of German phil-osophy' [...] "Are there any German philosophers? Are there any German poets?" Are there any good German books? - people abroad ask me these questions and I blush'. All that is left is a 'confounded instinct for mediocrity!' Nietzsche asks, 'How much beer is there in the German intellect' and he declares that 'the German spirit is growing coarser, it is growing shallower' and he asks, 'how is it that German seriousness, German profundity, German passion in spiritual things is more and more on the decline'. Ger-man culture suffers from 'a superabundance of presump-tuous journeymen and fragments of humanity, a spiritual instinct-atrophy'. Nietzsche can tell the Germans 'how many things they have on their conscience. They have on their conscience all the great crimes against culture for four centuries'. It is Germany that is responsible for 'national-ism, 'this most anti-cultural sickness and unreason'.

No-one, he says, 'can spend more than he has'. Thus 'if Germany spends itself on power, grand politics, economic affairs, world trade, parliamentary institutions, military interests - if it expends in these directions the quantum of reason, seriousness, will, self-overcoming that it has, then there will be a shortage in another direction. Culture and the state - one should not deceive oneself in this - are an-tagonists. The one prospers at the expense of the other'. Thus 'the rise of the 'Reich' signifies one thing above all, a displacement of the centre of gravity away from Ger-many'.

'Nothing as proud and hopeful as our own age has ever existed before [...] In 1871 the world was put to rights with the founding of Bismarck's Reich and this fact abolished all pessimistic philosophising'.

'The only culture I believe in is French culture and I consider all that is called culture elsewhere in Europe - to say nothing of German culture - a mere misconception

165

[...] Wherever Germany's influence extends, it corrupts culture.

'So far I have had very little enthusiasm for the German essence, but even less do I wish to keep this "magnificent" race pure. On the contrary, on the contrary'.

He calls himself 'a very good European', 'He who recognises values which he rates a hundred times higher than the welfare of the 'fatherland', of society, of blood-relations - values which are international and know no native country or race - such a man would be a hypocrite if he sought to play the patriot'.

He writes, 'What of our fatherland! Our helm wants to travel out and away, towards our children's land'.

'It seems to me that Germany for the last fifteen years has become a regular school of stupefaction: Water, rubbish, and filth, far and wide - that is what it looks like from a distance [...] However much it may bristle with arms like a hedgehog, I no longer have any admiration for it. It represents the most stupid, most depraved and most mendacious form of the German spirit that there has ever been - and what absurdities has not this spirit dared to perpetrate!'

The Germans were 'lying racial cheats, 'and 'rabble'.

'Does man have no higher duty than to the state? It may be that a man who sees his highest duty in serving the state really knows no higher duties but this is a relapse into stupidity; there are men and duties existing beyond this - and one of the duties is to destroy stupidity in all its forms, and therefore in this form too. There is something beyond the welfare of a state... '

'This nation has deliberately made itself stupid for practically a thousand years. Germany counts more and more as Europe's flatland [...] The moment that Germany rises as a great power, France gains a new importance as a cultural power [...] What the higher schools of Germany achieve is in fact a brutal breaking-in with the aim of making, in the least possible time, numberless young men fit to be utilised, utilised to the full and used up, in the state service'.

'I am myself now working on a memorandum for the European courts with a view to forming an anti-German league'.

He speaks of, 'bitter, old-maidenlike Germany' and grumbles that 'Goethe was always offensive to Germans. He had honest admirers only among Jewesses'.

And, inevitably, he homes in on music, 'I will never admit that a German can know what music means'.

'Those who we call German musicians, especially the greatest among them, are foreigners: Slavs, Croats, Italians, Netherlanders - or Jews'.

German taste is soon equated with the Wagner cult, 'When I last visited Germany, I found German taste exerting itself to grant equal rights to Wagner and to the most popular rubbish. Wagner is a sickness and has even made music sick' and the Germans have deceived themselves about him and his music, 'The Germans have constructed a Wagner for themselves whom they can venerate'.

Again, 'The German is foreign to liberality and kindness. The world and especially "Germania" I find increasingly repugnant. The Germans understand nothing, they are insensitive'. Nietzsche took more and more to reading French in preference to German, 'German books remind me of an untidy bedroom where you trip over things every time you take a step. The Germans are bad'.

'We must remember that Wagner was a young man when Hegel and Schelling were seducing men's spirits; that he had guessed and grabbed with his hands the one and only thing that Germans take seriously - "the idea" - that is to say, something obscure, uncertain, and full of intimations; that among the Germans clarity is an objection and logic a refutation'.

'Wagner's art requires one thing only -Teutons. Definition of a Teuton submission and long legs'.

He is not afraid to say that 'The Germans are the most

retarded civilised nation in Europe' and, in fact, insists that 'it is a part of my ambition to be considered a disdainer of the Germans par excellence. My mistrust of the German character I expressed even when I was twenty-six' (and he did, writing, 'anyone who has to live among the Germans suffers badly from the infamous greyness of their life and sense, their crudity, their dullness and oafishness, their awkwardness in delicate relationships and even more their envy and a certain deceitfulness and uncleanness in their character'). 'The Germans seem impossible to me. The Germans are canaille - how one lowers oneself when one associates with Germans, the Germans have no notion of how vulgar they are; but that is the superlative of vulgarity - they are not even ashamed of being merely Germans'. He adds, I seek among them for some sign of tact, of délicatesse in relation to me but in vain. From Jews, yes; from Germans never yet'.

'I have given the Germans the most profound books they have. This is reason enough for the Germans not to understand a single word'.

'Against the Germans I here advance on all fronts. You will need no complaints about "ambiguity". This utterly irresponsible race which has on its conscience all the great disasters of civilisation and at all decisive moments in history has something else on its mind [...] now has "the Reich" on its mind - this backsliding into petty state politics and cultural atomism - at a moment when for the first time the great question of values is being posed. There has never been a more important moment in history but who would be aware of that?'

Even in his final madness Nietzsche didn't forget his hatred of the Germans. In a letter to Burckhardt he wrote, 'Last year I was crucified by the German doctors in a very long and drawn-out manner' and in others he wrote to most of the courts of Europe telling them that he would be on his way to Rome on the following Tuesday and instructing them to be there to meet with him and the Pope. He sent a note to this effect to the Vatican telling them to expect him. There was one exception to this general invitation and that was the Hohernzollerns. He advised the courts of the other German princes to have nothing to do with them.

Of course a note should be added once again in respect of mirrors. Where Nietzsche is anti-German and pro-Jewish, Wagner is precisely the opposite.

Following Hitler's example, important members of the party came to visit the archive. Alfred Rosenberg, often called the philosopher of Nazism, a party member as early as 1919, had impressed Hitler because he was qualified. He had done what Hitler had failed to do, get into a college of architecture. He was made editor of the 'Völkischer Beobachter'. Hitler also appreciated his unrelenting anti-semitism and anti-Bolshevism. With Hitler as prop he remained the main race theorist of Nazism and was accepted as an expert in foreign affairs. He wrote relentlessly, his magnum opus being 'The Myth of the Twentieth Century'. This epic of some 700 pages sold half a million copies although Hitler was said to have tried it and failed. Schirach commented that Rosenberg was 'a man who sold more copies of a book no one ever read than any other author'.

Fritz Zeickel was another visitor. He had started out in a factory but worked his way up to become Gauleiter of Thuringia where he was renowned for his sadism. At the height of his power he was appointed as chief organiser of slave labour under the Third Reich. Then there was Balder von Shirack, a misguided romantic whose mother was American. He told his American guards at Nuremberg that he had espoused anti-semitism after reading a book by Henry Ford called 'The Eternal Jew'. Schirack became head of the Nazi youth movement and was later to become the hated Gauleiter of Vienna. Another visitor was Hans Frank, the head of the Nazi judiciary who wrote that 'the

169

National Socialist ideology is the foundation of all laws'. He became Bavarian Minister of Justice, Reichsminister without Portfolio and President both of the Academy of Law and the German Bar Association. He was Hitler's personal lawyer and later became governor of Poland where his equity shone through in such statements as, 'The Poles shall become the slaves of the Third Reich'. Schirer called him an 'intellectual gangster' and an 'icy, efficient, ruthless, bloodthirsty man'. Another visitor was Wilhelm Frick who Elizabeth had courted from the earliest days of Nazism. A dull bureaucrat, Frick was Hitler's dog and Hitler is famous for his love of dog's. Slavishly loyal, he accepted all sorts of unpleasant jobs that others refused. He was leader of the party in the Reichstag where he had been responsible for pushing through the Nuremberg laws against the Jews, communists and social democrats. This was the kind of visitor that Elizabeth welcomed with open arms.

She was now near the centre of power. From her secure position in Weimar she kept up a stream of propaganda on behalf of her fascist friends. In 1934, on June 14th, Hitler flew to Venice for a meeting with Mussolini. Dressed in a raincoat and felt hat, he looked insignificant beside Il Duce who sported a uniform and all his fascist regalia. The talks were not a success. Elisabeth sent each of them a telegram, 'The spirit of Nietzsche hovers over this meeting of the greatest statesmen of Europe'. To which she got replies, gratefully thanking her for her kind wishes and confirming that they had felt the spirit of Nietzsche hovering over them during their conversations. They told her that they had spoken of their admiration for Nietzsche and their respect for her as they made a boat trip to the Lido. A touch of mockery and a smile or two.

On his return from the Venice trip, Hitler made another visit to Weimar and to an Elizabeth who, at 88, could no longer be ignored. He stayed at the Hotel Elephant in the

Marktplatz. A huge crowd was there to see the dictator as he made his way from the hotel to the archive. He stepped out of the vestibule and into his black Mercedes which was facing left. He sat down waving to the adoring crowds as the car moved off and turned left into the Frauenstrasse. He would have seen the Goethe House immediately in front of him with its rows of fourteen windows in two tiers and driven slowly past Schillerstrasse on the right and the White Swan restaurant on the left. Then on past the Wielandplatz with its statue of the author, and right down the Sleuben-strasse and first left into the Humboltstrasse. Crossing the Trierstrasse, he would have continued slowly on up the hill to the archive which is at the top of the street on the right. A journey of minutes only.

She was waiting at the door of the villa with a deferential little group of visitors from around the world in a semi-circle behind her. She revelled in the meeting, grinning under her white lace cap while he, also enjoying himself, did a kind of dance in front of her something like, perhaps, the little dance he did in front of that railway carriage at Versailles before accepting a quite different kind of surrender. At least, in the photograph his arms and legs are blurred. A man in the crowd was impressed, 'So in the olden days might the great mother have greeted her great son. So might a prophet have received a hero, a great man the holy flame of a watchful priestess. No one who saw it will ever forget how the man to whom the whole world looks with the liveliest interest took his leave of the elegant old lady as they both stood in the bright sunshine'. On this occasion Elizabeth had a couple of presents for her mentor; the stick which Nietzsche had used on his walks in the mountains of the Engadine and, just to be consistent, a copy of the anti-semitic petition which Förster had presented to Bismarck 50 years before. Hitler had a very nice present for her too, access to his personal bank account.

Nietzsche had been resurrected and placed on a pedestal in a world he would have hated. Was he laughing somewhere at the way fate had treated him? He unwittingly

171

inspired so much that is second rate, so many littlenesses eating into a corpus still vibrant with the life of the mind. All making a living, raising to the top in the world's estimation by feeding off a body that refuses to die, that continues to give life, at second hand, to so many who end the lives of so many.

Today the Hotel Elephant is still there in the Weimar Marktplatz. Not at all a pushy building, it is easy to miss at first glance but, once inside, the pushiness almost hits you in the face. No longer as it was when visited by Goethe's Lotte whose appraising glance 'took in the starched mull curtains at the two windows, the gilt-framed console mirror, rather full and tarnished, between them; the two white-covered beds, sharing a little canopy, and the remaining conveniences of the bedchamber. The wall adorned with a copper-plate engraving and the well waxed floor that shone with cleanliness'.

That was in October 1816. In 1937 Fritz Zeickel wrote to the Chancellor to let him know that the hotel was about to fall to the ground. Naturally Hitler ordered a complete rebuild. He called on Hermann Giesler to do the job and gave him fairly detailed instructions. He wanted a hotel that 'demonstrates our feelings about life'. When the work was finished Hitler expressed satisfaction. You would know none of this today. In one of the corridors are memorabilia and pictures of all the honoured guests in the long history of the building. There are Bach, Goethe and Schiller, Thomas Mann and Von Weizsacker who had other problems. Kohl and Genscher and Vogel and, let's see, Lilli Palmer. Wagner is there, of course, as everywhere in this story. Do you notice a gap in this list? A certain skating around the edges?

From Weimar all traces of Nazism have been cleared away. Shops selling reproductions of old photographs of the town have hundreds of scenes of the place but among all this nostalgia there is no hint of a swastika on flag or armband. On the balcony of the famous National Theatre are the flagpoles from which the Nazi ensignia flew for all those years but are now gone. Perhaps the old people sitting warming themselves in the afternoon sun may remember a thing or two. Perhaps those famous statues of Goethe and Schiller, if they could speak, would have something to say. Incidentally, one of the attractions on its modern stage is 'Fiddler on the Roof'.

Resurrections come in peculiar forms. Elizabeth was far from being the only actor in Nietzsche's posthumous literary world. In 1951 another name was added to the list of books written by Nietzsche but this time, one he had written while mad, after his attack in Turin and while he was in the mental institution in Jena. It is called 'My Sister and I'. If the story is true, then it is his final book, his last will and testament, and has to take the place of Ecce Homo, itself a book often dismissed because written by a man who was on the verge of madness.

This new volume was published in New York and authenticated by no less a scholar than Dr Walter K. Stewart, 'an expert on Goethe and nineteenth century German literature,' and by the noted Nietzsche scholar, A. K. Placzek. How it came to see the light of day is a little too much like a detective mystery, like one of those complicated murders that take place in an Oxford college. A certain Oscar Levy received a communication from a young American journalist in London requesting a meeting to discuss a newly discovered work by the philosopher Nietzsche, a work, moreover, that is as much autobiographical as philosophical. They met the following day but the young man failed to bring the manuscript with him. It was in the hands of an ex-clergyman who was then in Canada where he had an interest in a rubber concern.

Not totally inappropriate considering the scandalous nature of the revelations which the document was supposed to contain.

This young man told a fascinating story. He had met the wife of this ex-clergyman who happened to be travelling on the same transatlantic liner to England. Weeks later he was contacted and asked to assist in a life threatening venture involving the woman, something to do with his helping her to return to Canada and which involved threats to his life. In return he was offered the manuscript which would be sent to him just as soon as the woman was safely in Montreal.

And how did this ex-clergyman get his hands on such valuable material. Another story. Soon after his entry into the asylum at Jena, Nietzsche decided to write one last book. Thus, although his faculties seemed to have deserted him because of his inability to make any kind of sense verbally, he could still write. He knew that Elizabeth had suppressed his last work, Ecce Homo, and that his mother was under her thumb ('for what extraordinary reason is it so frowned on by my family and withheld from publication') so he didn't want to entrust the new book to either of them. Instead he chose an inmate of the asylum, a businessman who, he was told, was soon to be discharged. It was this man who had succeeded in smuggling in the pens, paper and ink which Nietzsche had needed to do the writing and who left the place with the manuscript tucked away in his coat and with Nietzsche's instructions to get it to a publisher who would pay him handsomely for his troubles.

The man forgot both instructions and manuscript except to produce it every now and then and regale his friends with tales of the crazy Herr Professor who thought he was Jesus and Napoleon rolled into one. Finally he took it with him on a business trip to Canada where showed it to the ex-clergyman who was employing him in the rubber trade. On discovering that the man was interested in old books and manuscripts he produced his little treasure and was astonished to be offered a hundred dollars for it.

The ex-clergyman knew more philosophy than the businessman and proceeded to authenticate the manuscript. Already half convinced by the references to Jena and the mad professor, he checked the handwriting against published examples. Nietzsche's writing is really quite distinctive and he was convinced. He checked the style and the contents and became even more convinced. Even so he kept the manuscript for a whole year before offering it to the young journalist as a reward for helping get his young wife, a treasure of more value to him than any manuscript, back to Montreal. The journalist then approached Oscar Levy to translate the manuscript for him. Levy asked to see the manuscript but his wish was not granted and he returned to New York unsatisfied.

Can you imagine his surprise when, over two years later, the same papers landed on his desk. He translated and published the piece telling us in his introduction that 'the style is that of Ecce Homo'. All this in 1927. By the way, Levy's family deny any and all of this. They may have been put off by the nature of the text which contains quantities of soft porn quite un-Nietzsche like, 'I both loved and resented the wealth of warmth which Elizabeth brought to me in those unexpected hours of the night. I was usually in the midst of a sound sleep when she got into my bed, and thrilling as I found the ministration of her fat little fingers, it also meant that I was kept awake for hours and hours'. And elsewhere, 'It first happened between Elizabeth and me during the night that our young brother Joseph died, though we had no idea that he was dying when she crept into my bed, pleading that it was cold where she was, and she knew how warm I always was. [...] Suddenly I felt Elizabeth's warm little hands in mine, her hissing little voice was in my ear, and I began feeling warm all over'.

Anyway things go from peculiar to more peculiar. Levy sent his translation to the publisher Samuel Roth, another Jew, who advertised it as forthcoming in the 1928 series of 'Two Worlds Quarterly'. Roth was so highly thought of by his confrères that a petition was prepared against him with the signatures, amongst others of Lawrence, Hemmingway,

175

Eliot and Mann. Roth had published other books including, 'I was Hitler's Doctor, a sequel to 'Lady Chatterly's Lover' and another entitled, 'Jesus Must Live: An Account of the Persecution of the World by Israel on all the Frontiers of Civilization' which he had written himself. Sadly, however, his offices were visited by the New York Society for the Suppression of Vice. They were after James Joyce's 'Ulysses' but grabbed a quantity of other material including the Nietzsche. This American Society then proceeded to a complete an irreversible burning of the books in exactly the year that such things were going on elsewhere. Roth then, presumably dismayed by such illiterate activities, retired from publishing for some years leaving his documents stored in a warehouse. Much later, after the war and after Oscar Levy was so very conveniently no longer of this world, he returned to publishing and began to take an inventory of the stuff he had stored away. And, yes, he came across 'the brittle, vermin-eaten carbon copies of the translation' which had been 'further mutilated by careless handling'. He set to work to reconstruct the text setting several people to work on it. He even inserted footnotes 'hastily and without corroboration which caused much misunderstanding'.

As if all of Elizabeth's efforts had not been enough, we have this other footnote of forgery to deal with alongside hers. This time one which she would not have countenanced. It is perhaps nice to think that she didn't have a monopoly on recreations of her brother's image. Which brings us back to the main plot.

Elizabeth's health was now failing. In her eighty-ninth year she had an operation on her eye. While recovering in hospital she spent her time re-reading 'Mein Kampf', 'Those deeply strong perceptions and insights into the new creation of the German character took hold of me. I would advise any invalid to immerse himself in this wonderful book and to find strength and courage there to oppose the ordeals of fate'.

By then the Nietzsche Archive was firmly established, along with Bayreuth, as the twin centres of Nazi propaganda. But there remained one aim which Elizabeth had yet to accomplish. She still had to gain real recognition for Förster. She felt that his great service to Germany had gone unrecognised and was determined to correct it. It was now that she started to nag Hitler to recognised the man whose ideals had done so much to shape her own and beg him to raise her dear husband to an honoured place with other Nazi heroes alongside her brother. Of course she succeeded. Hitler agreed that Förster had earned the right to be buried under German soil and sent Uberbahnsturmführer Alfons Sachs or Shacks and gruppenführer Henrik Himmler to visit the grave in the Paraguayan jungle were Förster's body had been laid to rest nearly fifty years before and sprinkle the holy German soil over it. Like husband, like brother only the husband had never begged to be excused such ceremony. A new marble stone was erected over his body.

Hitler had now granted recognition to both halves of Elizabeth's existence and raised both of them from the dead to take their places among the heroes of Nazi mythology. How happy she must have been bustling about the archive in her eighties. Her brother was the famous thinker of the ruling class, her husband had been accepted as one of the fathers of their creed and the purity of the Aryan race seemed to be assured for ever. She never saw the things which would have made her really happy the final solution of the Jewish problem, the glorification of the race of blond heroes, the rule of Nazism over almost the whole of Europe, the raising of the Nordic myths to be the music which echoed through the age. We may rub our hands for just a second or two. She didn't die as happy as she might have died although she had seen her nation's solution to the problem of the Herero tribe in 1904. They were simply wiped out in a sort of practice run. 'Wrote General Lothar von Trotha, 'I believe that the nation as such should be annihilated' and again, 'I find it most appropriate that the nation should perish'. An officer wrote in his diary that 'nothing living was to be spared' and that 'this dealt with the extermination of the whole tribe'.

She died on November 9th 1935 at the grand old age of eighty-nine. Her body was found fully clothed on her bed by her housekeeper, Frau Balandkenhahn. She had felt tired and had gone to take a nap. Her soul, having dwelt for so long in the Platonic 'wholesome climate', having been for so many years 'in sympathy and harmony with the beauty of reason', was now freed from the rigours of perception and went wherever it went. From there, maybe, she could have been forced to see the success and collapse of all her hopes. And even, perhaps, their more recent resurrection.

In July 1945 the Americans had to give Weimar to the Red Army. They did so in the name of the allied troops that had entered the city three months before. On direct orders from Moscow the archive was sealed and remained unopened for nearly 50 years. Fifteen months later some of Elizabeth's friends and supporters, men who had visited her at the Archive, were hanged in the gymnasium of Nuremberg jail after a trial which had lasted months and had stunned the world. Thirteen shallow steps to the scaffold. Thirteen coils in the knot of the noose. Here they come: Ribbentrop who had a last wish 'that German unity should remain and that an understanding between East and West should come about, and peace for the world'. Keitel, 'I call on the Almighty to have mercy on the German people. Over two million went to their deaths before me. I now follow my sons. All for Germany'. Kaltenbrunner who regretted that crimes were committed in which he had no part. Alfred Rosenberg, the intellectual of Nazism, was almost at the point of collapse. Apart from answering to his name he said nothing. When a priest asked if he should pray for him he was told, 'No, thank you'. Wilhelm Frick remained silent. Hans Frank, dressed in a snappy tweed jacket, told his captors, 'I am grateful for the mild sentence I have been given. I pray God to receive me mercifully'. Steicher, 'Heil Hitler. Now I go to God'. Fritz Sauckel, Gauleiter of Thuringia who had read the oration at Elizabeth's funeral, 'I die innocent'. Jodl, 'I salute you, my Germany'. Last Seyss-Inquart limped up to the scaffold, 'I hope that this execution is the last tragedy of the Second World War'. Tragedy?

Goering had escaped execution by swallowing an ampoule of potassium cyanide earlier in the day. Echoes of other suicides, of Förster and of the führer both of whom he had so admired.

There is no official record of what happened to these eleven bodies. Their last sighting was in two vans with jeep escorts driving in the direction of Fürth where there was an airport. An official communiqué said that they 'had been cremated and the ashes disposed of'. Some believe that those vans went to Dachau which was an easy drive from Nuremberg and their cargo cremated in the ovens there. After all, even in their final moments, only Kaltenbrunner had shown any awareness that, just perhaps, a crime had been committed.

The communist regime in East Germany fell apart in November 1989 and the ban under which the archive had suffered was lifted. Suddenly the musty old place was opened to public view and the fresh air of a different world gusted through its imposing portals blowing light into dark corners. Here was the second coming of a slice of history which had been killed and interred for half a century. A great hoard of papers were opened to the public and that history could live again. The story of Elizabeth's rewriting and orchestration of her brother's work in the service of Europe's dictators was open to view. The resurrection of this tomb in Weimar revealed the body of Elizabeth's labours lying in state and waiting for another death, this time at the hand of academics living beyond the outstretched fingers of Nazi ideology.

Posthumous Existences

An endless story of resurrections or at least of conversions. Attempts to bring people home from exiles misunderstood. Make them like us. Change them. Jews into Christians or corpses. Brown men in their homes in the heart of darkness into Christians or corpses. Nietzsche into something he never was - a man who believed in all this conversion while he had in fact fought all his life for quite a different kind of resurrection - a death of God announced by a madman who comes into the square carrying a burning lantern under the midday sun. A woman so very eager to be converted who in her hurry converts his writings into their opposites and her brother into a warrior for Nazism. Blanchot wrote, 'How strange it is that the greatest literary glories of our time should be born of entirely posthumous works; Kafka, Simone Weil, Hopkins; or partially so as with Hölderlin, Rimbaud, Lautréament, Trakl, Musil, and, in a crueller sense, Nietzsche'. And he adds, 'One would like to recommend to writers - don't leave anything behind you, destroy yourself all that you wish to see disappear; do not be weak, do not put your faith in anyone; you will necessarily be betrayed one day'.

Nietzsche asks: 'Why is it that from Plato onwards every philosophical architect in Europe has built in vain?' and, if this is the case, then are we not in a posthumous philosophy today, beyond the closure of the history of all those philosophical architects, a closure the beginning of whose end was brought about by none other than Nietzsche himself? But is any such beyond possible and, if so, how can we still think of posthumous existences?

And then there is the little problem of the eternal recurrence of the same which seems, surely, to deny all endings and beginnings and, along with them, all posthumous existences. Here is Heine again, 'according to the eternal laws that control the combinations of this eternal play of repetitions, however much time may pass, all configurations that have heretofore existed on this earth must still meet, attract, repel, kiss, and cor-rupt each other again'. Then it must be that you have wanted back that moment that is passing even in its passing. You want, more than that, you will it to pass again and again. The other side of closure is a place forbidden to thought.

Nietzsche, of course, called himself a posthumous thinker but he did not mean by this that we would reading about him and pulling his sentences apart after his death when constantly changing interpretations would be demanded. Rather he meant that he was untimely. Great art is made through intoxication, the intoxication of spring, of sex, of the brave deed, even of cruelty. With this intoxication of desire, of will, 'one amplifies everything out of one's own abundance'. The moment of creation is nothing other than a dive into the future, a making the future present and a creating, not a recreating, of the past. Eternal recurrence denies consequitive reason which ticks away in the discrete moments of clock time. What might happen has already happened in one moment which occurred 'six thousand feet beyond man and time' - in 1881, a reversible date - where the world and its just-ifications fall away, a moment which draws into itself both past and   future and 'transforms every "it was" until it will say: "but I willed it thus! thus shall I will it"'. Or as Theodore Herzl put it somewhat later, 'If you will it, it is no dream'.

It might, of course, also have meant something rather different to a man with intimations of his own syphilitic mortality. The child of a father who died of softening of the brain and left him fatherless. The father of no child. The man who had to become a childless father. The self that had to be overcome was a self 'without a father' and without any son other than text which flowed or over-

flowed from the eternal moment. This self whose paternity was syphilitic, which had at its core intimations of
mortality from both directions, could do nothing other
than retire into the eternal moment of negative capabi-
lity and be 'left to bleed at sacrificial altars'. Posthumous
existences will always be ours not his and the more so
the less he is understood. No wonder, then, that it was
left above all to Elizabeth to ferment eternal recurrence
into a Nazi brew.

The remains of history are taken up and changed. Mani-
pulation for the sake of a history quite at odds with the
place where it lay for centuries. The Ahnenerbe or Ances-
tral Heritage Society, a department of Himmler's SS, were
given the task of recreating history in their own Nazi image and discovered the origins of civilisation in the distant
Neolithic past of Germany. As the legend has it, 'The journey began before time when the last gods transfered their
secrets to the first human beings in an icy country at the
edge of the world. Some called this place Thule, others believed it to be Atlantis and the people who learned the secrets of the gods were know as Germans'.

Incidentally, of the heads of the forty-six departments of
Himmler's organisation, nineteen had doctorates and another nineteen were full professors, many with international
reputations. The allied report on the society concluded
that they were, 'engaged in a project to rewrite the past in
order to influence the future course of history' which is
not so unlike Elizabeth's rather smaller project.

Back to that Nietzsche of the Archive who may not be
entirely sane. He lay in bed, propped up on a pile of pillows so like Heine on his mattress grave. He was dressed
in a flowing white gown which gave him the appearance
of an ancient philosopher or, maybe, the inmate of some

182

asylum. His hands rested on the coverlet, one of them half clenched and slightly twisted, the other open with thumb and first finger gently touching. His hair was brushed firmly back over his head and his enormous moustache was combed in exactly the opposite direction, down over his mouth, covering it completely. His shoulders and upper body rested on the pillows but his head was held upright and his deep eyes stared out towards the left of the picture and followed the setting sun.

In his last years Nietzsche was always drawn facing the setting sun. watching the setting sun. Like that sun and perhaps that ailing philosopher, Zarathustra, he also wanted to go down, 'now he sits here and waits, old shattered law tablets around him and also new tablets - half written'. The older and madder he got, the more pictures we have of him and those made after he could no longer object to them are as strange as the lack of them earlier. He is both present and absent. Another Satan fallen from glory, he shines like the setting sun he so often watched from the balcony at Weimar or like a sun eclipsed, a light dissipated and thus more wonderful, much more wonderful, than the clear light of midday.

What can we discover by speaking of a likeness? What impossible irrelevant baggage does every detail drag along in its wake? We speak here of his black eyes and instantly know him to be deep and passionate, potentially mad. We describe a high forehead and presume great intelligence or are forced to acknowledge a high forehead because we speak of Nietzsche. And that contemplative stare into the distant sunset must, of course, be the inward stare of the philosopher. Of what help can all this be? With Nietzsche every possible chance was taken to hide behind an image which was false and deceptive which is why there were, perhaps, so few portraits or photographs. The picture of himself which we read in his texts is intense by its very falsity, is intended to convince and thus to mislead. The image that he gives us is only what we see and the only help he gives is helping to mislead.

183

But why bother with the likeness? Is not the likeness there in the text jumbled up amongst the words and their meanings? Well, with Nietzsche no excuses are needed. He lives in his texts. Lazarus can raise himself to a posthumous existence. The fire of an impossible future is always there between the words and even in the books he will never have time to write. He repeatedly thought up a stream of new title pages, writing to his friends and even out of the blue to people he had never met with further outpourings of plans and projects stretching into the ...

Impossible. It can't be done. He sits there staring out of the window at the setting sun. Another retreat. There is no following him. The books also constantly shift, go out of focus and fall back into the shadows in order to make us squint and stare so much the harder. He was always the exception, the friend who lived in loneliness behind a thousand masks. He wore a different one for each occasion. No two portraits of him are alike and the portraits which he paints of himself are also mirages which waver and disperse and re-appear transformed. And yet there are descriptions although not many. For Dr Paneth, 'He has an unusually high forehead, smooth brown hair, wan, sunken eyes - as is natural in someone half blind - bushy eyebrows, quite a full face, clean-shaven, apart from a heavy moustache'. For Meta von Salis he has 'a quiet melodious voice and his extreme soft-spokenness, made an immediate impact [...] When a smile illumined his face, bronzed in the fresh Mediterranean air, the expression was movingly childish, inviting involvement'. And Lou Salomé was impressed by his 'noiseless way of talking', his 'neat style of dressing', and his 'cautious, wistful gait, shoulders slightly rounded [...] He gave the impression of standing to one side, alone'. And here is a description of 1875 from Ludwig von Scheffler, 'He was of small rather than middle stature [...] the iridescent glasses and deep moustache gave his face that impression of intellectuality which often makes even short men somewhat imposing'.

Earlier he had been a bit of a dandy. At Basle he attracted notice because of his overdressing. He was described as being a little below average height, solidly built. He was the only man in the town to flaunt a grey topper except for an old state councillor from Baden. He already sported the famous moustache, perhaps to hide his youth. There is a shot of him taken in 1865 which shows it already in place. From then on it grew bigger and bigger. It was already growing during the stay in Basle. By 1882 there is the picture in which it completely covers his lower lip and in another of 1892, taken with his mother, it has grown to cover his entire chin.

He hated the photographer. In 1888, Georg Brandes pleaded with him to have a likeness taken because he was 'extremely anxious to know what you are like in appearance'. Nietzsche had to admit that he hadn't got a single one to send as 'my sister, who has married and gone to America has taken with her the last photographs of myself that I possessed' and he refused, 'I entertain a profound mistrust of ordinary photographers'. Later he relented and asked a friend to send one on to Brandes. This was finally received but was 'a profile picture, characteristic in outline but with far too little expression' and, Brandes complained, 'Surely you must look different from that'.

And there are other photographs. There is one from 1864 where he is posing in a studio at the age of 17, leaning against a pedestal which is also shared by a huge vase of sprouting greenery. No moustache yet, his hair sleeked down, hand tucked Napoleon-like into his neat frock coat. Expression serene but confident. Three years later and another abstracted image, a head and shoulder affair with no background. Glasses now, metal framed and elongated so that the eyebrows show above them, the hair still short and close to the head. The heavy lower face with its slight sneer because, as his medical notes later mention the right corner of his mouth turned down somewhat. This the moustache was later to hide although Lou Salomé speaks of his 'beautiful mouth'. Another, this time as a horseman with the field artillery, very military in baring, dressed in uniform with sword at the ready, hair and glasses the same but now the moustache very much in evidence. And then the wonderful grainy figure taken in 1871 in Lugano. Again no background but this time jaunty with heavy overcoat, the collar raised against the weather and a bowler perched above it. Arms folded in front of his chest. Moustache still there and still somewhat military and the same glasses. The suspicion of a smile.

Another from 1882, one of those typically Victorian set pieces and not a little ludicrous. Nietzsche with Paul Rée and Lou von Salomé. All three of them look as stiff as statues while posing in a way which they must have thought natural. Rée and Nietzsche are holding the holster of a cart, Rée staring direct to camera and Nietzsche glancing off to the right, the reverse of his usual direction. Lou is kneeling in the cart itself holding what looks like a toy whip. All three of them have embarrassing smiles. Behind them is a studio landscape, an oak tree to the right and a cloud to the left. The two men are dressed smartly in suits and bow ties. The idea was Nietzsche's. They had arrived together at the studio of Monsieur Bonnet and discovered the cart which was there to give a touch of rural reality to his pictures. Nietzsche was struck by the thing and had it brought centre stage for the first and probably only time in its photographic history. He insisted on Bonnet finding a piece of rope which was placed around his left and Rée's right arm and held by Lou who was placed kneeling in the cart. The little whip was made out of a piece of stick and some spare rope. Thus the famous montage which Nietzsche thought best represented the relationship of the three friends. There is another portrait picture of Nietzsche clearly taken at the same session; same bow tie and coat, same fuzzy grain. It is inscribed to Lou from 'Friedrich Nietzsche, formerly a professor now a roaming fugitive'.

Finally, before he vanishes altogether, Nietzsche's head moves even further to the right and almost out of the picture. Now a black statue, he is still looking out beyond the frame to his left but all except his forehead and that huge walrus moustache, are out of the picture. Now, between him and the beautiful setting sun, a figure imposes itself, a figure dressed in a uniform with black hair sleeked down across its forehead and a small toothbrush moustache. Everything in him is Nietzsche's opposite; the tiny moustache, the thin hair brushed forward, the small shifty eyes. And he looks away from the sun. Their eyes cannot meet.

Eyes that do not meet. And in the background is a figure dressed in mourning who presides over this event. She holds her head high and her chest out and in her hand, as always, is a small umbrella. For her this is a moment of great pride, this encounter in which there is no meeting, in which even Nietzsche's statue has almost absented itself, leaving behind only his nose and moustache as tokens. From this encounter, from this non-encounter, the written word has vanished from the page like Nietzsche's head from the picture and it has become, except for tokens, invisible.

Did the ceiling above Elizabeth's burgeoning archive, the ceiling upon which the steps of the madman trod back and forth represent so radical a break? Were those footfalls in another world or in ours? Was Nietzsche a lost soul pacing across the rocks of a Hades above the world of the living? Did his afterlife contradict his life? Nietzsche himself thought not. He had already said that there was no such thing as a radical break in a man's life. However forcefully a man or Nietzsche himself seems to leap from one contradiction to another, close observation will always reveal the dovetailing. Earlier he had written a little conversation between A and B in which A had said, "You are removing yourself faster and faster from the living; soon they will cut you off their list" to which B had answered, "It is the only way of sharing the privilege gained by the dead" and A had asked, "What privilege?" and B had answered, "To die no more". Again, 'Now that the affirmative part of my task is done, it is the turn of the denying, the No-saying and No-doing part'.

187

But then of course this thought itself was lodged in the world of the living and might not be able to force its way into the consciousness of Hades, of the other world. Metaphysical frenzy is suffocating, 'it has at last reached the point where I could feel it pressing on my throat as though it would suffocate me'.

And Nietzsche had enough to say about madness before he went mad. Just as the Christians say that death is rebirth, that the life of the living merely a preparation for the posthumous existence of a land of shadows, so Nietzsche thought of madness before he went mad, 'The madman is a mask and speaking trumpet of divinity' and, 'The madman crosses a divide between the old and stale, between the world we already know and think we understand and the world of the dead which is the new world, the world of Montezuma which Cortez never reached'. Again, 'Madness prepares the way for the new idea and the prophet immolates himself upon it'. And again, 'Everyone who is profound loves a mask [...] and behind the mask is not only cunning but within the cunning an abundance of good [...] a man who is so elusive and whose instinct is to use speech for silence and concealment and is inexhaustible in eluding communication, wants to replace himself with a mask so as to roam among the heads and hearts of his friends and thus makes certain that he does so. [..] Every deep spirit needs a mask - more, around every deep spirit a mask is perpetually growing' and later, 'please give me - What? What? Say it! - one more mask! A second mask!' This hiding behind masks, this wanting to hide behind masks, is also a danger, 'How can we find ourselves?' he asks, 'How can man know himself? He is a dark and veiled thing [...] It is a tormenting, dangerous beginning to dig down into oneself in such a way and to force one's way down the well of one's being [...] The man who does this can easily do so much damage to himself that no physician will be able to cure him'.

It seemed as if he was putting a mask between himself and the real world, as if he was using a pseudonym behind which he could hide his real feelings. Gast felt that

Nietzsche did not want to be drawn forth from behind his similar kind of mask. He would refuse all such attempts. From Ecce Homo, 'The eye of the sun just fell upon my life [...] How could I fail to be grateful to my whole life?' and, 'Now I bid you lose me and find yourselves'.

Gast wrote, 'I believe that Nietzsche would be about as grateful to his rescuers as somebody who has just jumped into the water to drown himself and has been pulled out by some idiot of a lifesaver'. Gast felt that he did not want to be cured, 'It seemed - horrible though it is - as if Nietzsche were merely feigning madness, as if he were glad for it to have ended in this way'.

In that long journey since Plato, the new has always been heralded by madness and distrusted, martyred and destroyed. In the ancient world the new man, the framer of new laws, the messenger of the new morality, if he was not already mad, had to pretend to be mad or to make himself mad. The madder the man the more he was admired. The saint who vanished into the desert and draped himself in sackcloth, spending his months and years fasting on top of a pillar. The hermit who shed his courtly clothes and retired to sit under a tree. The lady who gave all her wealth to the poor and passed the rest of her days in a little cell build on to the side of an insignificant church. And what were all of these committed to but madness. They contemplate only what can bring on 'ecstasy or disorders of the mind'. They prayed to the powers of heaven to bring on deliriums and convulsions, sudden lights and darkness 'until I crawl like a beast of the field'. If the new message does not come from out of the old, if it can make no sense to the living then it must come from you, from the lord of hosts or I am nothing'.

Once he awoke suddenly and surprised all those at his bedside by crying out loudly 'Blessed be almighty God, who has favoured me with this great blessing. His mercies are indeed boundless, nor can the sins of men limit or hinder them'. To one of those who were sitting with him these words seemed more rational than his general speech before his illness and she asked, 'of what mercies, do you speak and of what sins of men?' He answered that the

189

mercies of which he spoke were those that God showed him at this moment and that allowed him to think at last without impediment and had cleared his mind from the mists of ignorance to which his continuous reading of books had led him, 'Now I understand their absurdities and deceptions. Now that I am approaching the end I should like to meet it so as to leave the world convinced that my life has not been that of a madman'.

'The perception of tortured genius who suffers horribly for the sake of his vision skimming along the surface above depths of madness is probably accurate' writes Dr Post, a modern psychiatrist who, 'having looked at the lives of nearly 300 famous men, believes exceptional creativity and psychiatric problems are intertwined. He concludes that philosophers in the severe class include Kierkegaard, Cardinal Newman, Ruskin, Marx and Nietzsche. Among composers he mentions Wagner ... '

Escape is from the world of suffering to another world where suffering and contempt are defeated. All Nietzsche's writings are located at the exact point at which these two worlds meet. At the point where the one world is brought to heel and the new world imposed upon it. Overcoming suffering, 'What cannot kill me makes me stronger. The more I suffer the more suffering is defeated and the greater sanity of another sphere is made possible'. From the mythic nonsense of Elizabeth's museum to the living footfalls of Nietzsche dying in his Hades just above the floorboards. He writes to his doctor, 'My existence is a dreadful burden and I would have thrown it off long ago if I had not been making the most instructive tests and experiments on mental and moral questions in just this condition of suffering and almost complete renunciation'. This pleasurable thirst for knowledge which carries him to heights at which he conquers all torment and hopelessness makes him happier than ever before. Brandes writes in his obituary, 'After thirsting for recognition to the point of morbidity, he attained it in an altogether fantastic degree when, though still living, he was shut out from life'.

Or into life. For anyone versed in dialectics, deception is crucial for, 'without it, how can a person be deceived into the truth?' Kierkegaard understood this perfectly and used deception to 'bring into the truth one who is in an illusion'. Direct communication supposes that the hearer is able to hear but if an illusion stands in the way and deafens him , masks and pseudonyms are needed, the writer must hide his truth behind a mask and step out into the illusion of his audience in order to have the power to speak to them and give them the chance to understand him. But, of course, this also means that he may step back again behind the mask into the truth and refuse to speak any more.

Perhaps a man who is 'but mad North-north-west' and who can see the tiny demons fluttering over the shoulders of the guilty can prophecy against the horrors that he knows will come. The little man stands there in front of him, this little man like so many thousands of little men who have killed god and already taken the first steps from which they will never return. Facing the prophet who can ask him, unseeing yet seeing so many horrors in that bland actor's eyes, 'How could we drink up the sea? Who gave us the sponge to wipe away the entire horizon? What were we doing when we unchained this earth from its sun? Whither is it moving now? Whither are we moving? Away from all suns? Are we not plunging continually. Backwards, sideways, forwards, in all directions? Is there still any up and down? Are we not straying as through an infinite nothing? Do we not feel the breath of empty space?'

Thus spoke the madmen who had the audacity 'to light a lantern in the bright morning hours' in which so many others thought they lived. Across that final photograph glares the lion's head in stone that fails to see the little man with his little moustache and his hair brushed forward who stares at him with such an appearance of reverence but who certainly had never read a single word of his warnings. That glare of stone saw so much more.

Binswanger's original diagnosis was that Nietzsche's madness did not come on suddenly but had been developing for a long while. He noted Nietzsche's own comment that his father had suffered from the same illness. His mother wrote to Overbeck quite early on, while Nietzsche was in his first days at Jena, that she had read through the 'Twilight of the Ghosts' (as she called it) and comments that, 'it is enough to torment anyone's brain and I suppose the others are just like it'. She takes it along to Binswanger as an aid to him in diagnosing Nietzsche's illness.

The few and the many, the Master and the slave. Nietzsche became more and more antagonistic to the many and wrote increasingly for an audience that dwindled to nothing.

To Meysenbug, 'I have unreeled my line to "the few" instead of the many and I did this even without "impatience". Soon even the few were discarded in favour of the none. I speak only to myself more and more. A steady withdrawal from any communication with the world. Into madness?'

To Reinhard von Seydlitz, 'If I have been speaking to almost no one it has not been a 'proud silence' but, on the contrary, a very humble one, that of a sufferer ashamed to reveal how much he suffers. An animal crawls into its burrow when it is sick; so does la bête philosophe. How rarely a friendly voice reaches me! I am now alone, absurdly alone. And in the course of my relentless underground war against everything men have until now honoured and loved, imperceptibly I myself have unwittingly become something of a burrow, something hidden that can no longer be found even when you go out and look for it. But no one goes out to look for it. Confidentially, it is not impossible that I am the leading philosopher of this epoch, and perhaps even a little more than that, something decisive and fateful standing between two epochs. But one is made to pay constantly for such an isolated position - with an isolation that is growing evermore icy, ever more cutting'.

As early as 1876 he wrote to Gersdorff about the Christmas that has just passed, 'I have just been through the worst, most painful, most dismal Christmas I have ever known. On the very first day, after numerous danger signals, there was a real breakdown. I could no longer doubt that I was in the throes of a serious disease of the brain, and that only this centre could cause so much pain in my stomach and eyes'. And he added despairingly, 'My father died of brain fever at thirty six; it's possible that I'll go even sooner'.

To Georg Brandes, 'Just now a choral work of mine with orchestra called "A Hymn to Life" is being published. It is intended to go down to posterity and to be sung one day "in memory of me" assuming of course that enough of me survives to be remembered. You see on what posthumous thoughts I am existing. A philosophy like mine is like a tomb - it seals one off from the living. 'He who hides well has lived well', that is what is written over the grave of Descartes '. An epitaph (stolen from Horace) if ever there was one.

To Carl Fuchs, 'Throughout the last years the vehemence of my inner vibrations has been frightening. Now

193

that I have to move on to a new and higher form of expression, I need first of all a new sense of alienation, a even greater depersonalisation ... '

To Gast, 'All my previous life has been ruled off at this point [...] truly until now my existence has shown itself to be what it really is - a mere promise.

He had become another or was pretending to be another. He scribbled notes transferring the first and third persons. He wrote down that, 'He is very happy to have visitors' and that, 'He recognises voices from earlier times'. Even in his madness rewriting himself.

As his sister rewrote Nietzsche so Nietzsche scribbled what she was thinking, 'I am monstrously good'. And he referred on her behalf to the colony in Paraguay as if she was speaking of her colonising over him and her precious archive beneath his feet, 'As mother of the colony I still have much to do for all the colonists. God has always helped me. I am very glad to give'.

Madness, like labyrinths or mazes, are designed to confuse like the most famous of all labyrinths, the one at Crete (a labyrinth which, as we know, preyed on Nietzsche's mind). From this confusion there is only one sure way out and that is to return by the way we have come following Ariadne's thread. But to return thus step by step exactly by the way we have come is to find our way back through our mother's womb to the nothingness from whence we came. And this, as we know, is contrary to human nature. Our return does not turn back but forward, ever onwards towards the nothingness beyond death which is not the same as the nothingness before existence for the reason that it incorporates existence, a hundred thousand acts which we have reeled out behind us. Living leaves a trail, a trace, which, even dead, we can hardly efface. Every life, indeed every act, has a posthumous existence, has affects, which it cannot retrieve or alter or even deny. Life is forever with his hand at his lips bidding adieu. Death is merely another form of this inevitable move-ment. To cower beneath such a mountain of actions, of words, of loves and hates, is already a kind of madness or confusion or loss and finally, with a sigh (whether heavy or light we are too far away to hear) to turn away, to drop the thread, to give up Ariadne and all she stands for and stand in the gloomy passageway of the labyrinth waiting for ...

Or like some insomniac who, after shifting this way and that through the darkest reaches of the night, finally finds a comfortable position on the pillow and can get some sleep.

Elizabeth tells us that her brother enjoyed the lovely view from his window. He could see Weimar and the mountains beyond and further off that 'the wide horizon with its cloud forms and sunsets'. Elizabeth tells us that 'his happiest hours were spent on the front veranda' and 'how he rejoiced every day in the beautiful view over Weimar and the lights on the Ettersberg hills'. It was in those Ettersberg hills with their woods of beeches towards which the mad philosopher gazed that the Germans built the concentration camp known as Buchenwald, an exer-cise amongst other things, in how hard work and devo-tion to duty can create opposites.

For not so long after Elizabeth had finished busying herself turning Nietzsche's philosophy inside out, over there in those hills towards which her dying brother had

gazed, other devoted men had done marvels with opposites, building huge cities of the dead with the labour of
men hardly alive.

And how were these human creatures done away with?
Well here's how. By convincing them that quite the
opposite was happening, that they were going to a shower
house or a medical examination. Out there at Buchenwald, quite close to the gnarled Goethe oak which the
builders left in place in reverence to German culture, the
prisoners were pushed one at a time through a kind of medical procedure carried out by men in white coats with
encouraging smiles on their faces. But when they stood on
a slatted surface to have their height measured and one of
the assistants was busying himself with the equipment, a
dull shot would ring out and a body would slump to the
floor. Why? Because hidden behind the wall on which the
measuring rod had been nailed was a little chamber with
a table and a magazine and an SS guard with a pistol. His
job was to raise the pistol at regular intervals and shoot a
bullet into the back of the neck of the man, woman or
child on the other side of the wall who was in the middle
of his medical and standing straight as he could to help
his doctors. The body was then removed and the blood
washed away ready for the next examination. Over the
gates at Buchenwald were the words, 'My country right or
wrong'. In the magazine were, quite possibly, quotes from
Nietzsche. As for other medical experiments conducted
by real doctors in Ward 46 at Buchenwald ('well equipped
and a model of cleanliness') with instruments and sup-
plies donated by some of the biggest names in German
pharmacology, both business and professional, the more
said the better.

Buchenwald is, of course, another posthumous existence
for it is still there like the confessional in the shadows of
the nave of a cathedral dedicated to a god who is still sort

196

of alive. You can get to it by road from Weimar although there is a slight suspicion that the signposts are not as accurate as they might be. The journey is pleasant enough and takes you on a gentle climb through pine forests until you arrive at a huge open area. A desire to take a deep breath for more than one reason but at least partly because the forest falls away on three sides and the sky, deep blue, seems to pulse upwards and away also. Expansiveness and space, the very opposite of oppression. The site is beautiful. Of course, the place is a tourist attraction now, one of the reasons that people from all over the world come to Weimar. Areas for parking; here for coaches and there for cars. Little arrows directing you to the various sites. The museum with its mock-ups of the huts in which so many thousands lived and died not one of which remains, the cabinets of uniforms and tools and documents and so much else which we can stare at in a sort of horror that is numbed so that it may not be felt. They have the chamber where doctors organised the murder of their patients. At the perimeter a few small buildings where the inmates were processed. The ovens stand oddly silent and cold with a few flowers on the floor in front of them. The trolleys for the bodies still standing motionless on their rails. Outside the gentle hills fall away on all sides. The sun shining in a clear sky. One of the hottest days of the year and yet here everyone was shivering. Visitors standing about in silence. Schoolgirls in tears.

Hovering over these horrors was - nothing. For no God could allow such things to happen, allow such madness to take the form of meticulous control of every detail. No. It was clear. As the power of Satan had steadily increased, the power of God had slowly died. God was dead. Do we need a madman to tell us that 'We have killed him - you and I. All of us are his murderers [...] God is dead. God remains dead and we have killed him'. And to continue,

197

'How shall we comfort ourselves, the murderers of all murderers? [...] Who will wipe this blood off us? What water is there for us to clean ourselves?' Nietzsche puts himself in the place of the Judas who kissed god and took his blood upon himself and upon his children.

And what replaces the God who is now in his grave and for whom we are singing a kadesh, a requiem aeternam deo? Why, of course, it is the superman and not the one who flies through the air and wears his pants outside his trousers but another much more dangerous one. Nietzsche writes of his ubermensch or overman, 'The overman is the meaning of the earth' or, 'is it not the time, now that the type "herd animal" is being evolved more and more in Europe, to make the experiment of a fundamental, artificial and conscious breeding of the opposite type and its virtues?' or again, 'There is only nobility of birth, only nobility of blood' or, 'the conviction that one has duties only to one's equals, towards the others one acts as one thinks best'.

This is what the Nazis liked to think and to quote and use to justify... and yet these snippets are embedded in something so much more difficult as Nietzsche also tells us, 'never yet has there been an overman' and why? Because to be overman is to be ... almost an impossibility, 'the man who has overcome himself has become an overman' and he writes on the title page of Ecce Homo, 'How one becomes what one is'. The Nazi is the reverse of this because he follows, he does his duty. What was it that they all said like a mantra at Nuremberg? - 'I was only doing my duty'. The follower is passive, he does nothing, there is nothing for him to overcome. Even his God is not worth killing. Is this the Nazi? Does he 'desire no praise'? Does he have 'care for most external things?' does he avoid 'petty honours and mistrust all those who are ready in their praise'? Does he 'protect artists and poets?' Does he have 'disgust for the demagogic?' and finally does he 'love him who lives for knowledge and who wants knowledge so that one day the ubermensch may live. And thus wills his own downfall?'.

And what, you may well ask, about the will to power? How does that fit in with the constant and dramatic deconstruction of the posthumous existences which smash dreams and create echoes which sound so very different from the original and formidable shout sent out across the canyons of the years? Well, how indeed? Is this yet another and particularly frightening example of Nietzsche's famous irony, of the invisibility which faith demands? Or is the will to power merely the promise of yet another existence about which we can do nothing and in the face of which we should resign all gnashing of teeth and grant ourselves a gentle smile? For history is the muse which Hegel followed with a smile and which rules our lives from afar. Fighting it is a smaller sign of virility than succumbing to its forces which are considerable and can destroy nations. 'The expropriators of history' Marx might just as well have said, 'will be expropriated' and bring down on their heads a terrible fury.

That which will happen anyhow, in spite of the greatest drive to will it, is what we must accept just as we must accept the impossibility of altering the horrors of the past, of wanting and willing just those horrors. The creative will must say to it, "But I willed it thus!" and again, "'But I will it thus! Thus shall I will it!'" I must will even the destruction of all that I most profoundly will. This is the will to power which has reached the final extent of its own power.

Is there, hidden away somewhere behind those penetrating eyes a premonition of his sister's betrayal? How well, after all, he must have known her. Did he persuade himself that even such horrors as were still to come must be willed as an inevitable inversion of what is merely wanted, of what is merely written? God had turned away his face so there was no other will behind such horrors other than the lonely philosopher's desperate knowledge that

199

the very things he wanted most would be twisted into their opposites and multiplied to the very edge of the possible. Is that the will to power: the love of that beyond all understanding, even that of Nietzsche himself?

Rebirths and unquiet graves and posthumous existences and Christian and Jew bring another story creeping to the fore, that of Zvi Michalowsky who was unlucky enough to have been in Eysyski on the day of the New Year in 1941 when the Jews of the place were taken in groups of 250 to the old Jewish cemetery and lined up naked in front of open ditches where they were shot in the back of the head by their Lithuanian guards.

So frightened was he that he fell forward a second before the bullet hit him. He lay there in the pit as the bodies fell into it on top of him. When the shooting stopped he was left there, presumed dead. He waited until dark and then, like Lazarus and he who brought Lazarus to life, arose, alive and stumbled out of the grave and into the night. Shivering with the cold he made his way to the hamlet where he could see the shape of the church around which, he knew, were the homes of the Christian people of the village who knew him well.

He knocked on the first door which, after a moment, opened. 'Please let me in' he begged. The peasant lifted up his lantern throwing its light on the naked body covered in blood. 'Jew', he told him, 'go back to the grave where you belong' and shut the door in his face. The poor man tried one house after another but always there was the same response until he came to one a little apart from the rest nearer to the forest where an old widow lived. When she opened the door to his knocking she had in her hand a burning piece of wood. 'Let me in' begged Zvi and she replied as had all the others 'Jew, go back to the grave where you belong' and chased him away with the burning branch as if she were exorcising an evil spirit.

But Zvi turned around and faced her, 'I am your Lord Jesus Christ come down from the cross', he told her, 'Look at me - the blood, the pain, the suffering of the innocent! Let me in'. At this the widow crossed herself and fell on her knees at his blood-stained feet. 'My God, My God' she kept repeating. After a while she got herself together and opened the door for him.

Zvi entered. He promised to bless her children, her farm and her but only if she kept his visit a secret for three days and three nights and didn't reveal it to a living soul, not even to the priest. She fed him and washed him and gave him some clothes. Before he left he told her once again that the Lord's visit must on no account be revealed because of His special mission on earth.

Dressed, clean and fed he made his way to join the partisans in the forest.

While Nietzsche was enjoying the beautiful view over the Ettersberg hills he was allowed the occasional visitor. They describe his 'high forehead, the bushy eyebrows, the noble, deep eyes and the strong, hanging moustache'. Again, 'The forehead, the mighty forehead, the strongly protruding lower face, the nose, very delicate and elegant. Thick hair, completely black and soft as silk, like a woman's. Eye sockets deep, quite expressionless'. His eyes were not extinguished, 'dark and velvety in the depths of the fine and richly arched brows'. His features were as if chiselled, except that the moustache grew beyond the line of the mouth.

Elizabeth speaks warmly of the improvements which she saw in her brother because of the move to this new house, 'The lofty, sunny sitting rooms and bedrooms, the comfortable bathroom and the winter veranda at the rear of the house also pleased him immensely. He had always said that his constitution was made for light and air, and now his words were being proved true in an unexpected

201

way. He began to hold conversations again and comment on what was read to him and even tried to write - a feat made impossible for years by the paralysis of his right side'. She wrote as if Nietzsche was a quite normal invalid, physically fit and astute to the last 'He kept his politeness and affability to the end, understood everything that went on around him, listened to what was read to him very attentively and sometimes even chose the books he wanted to have read'. Elizabeth, of course, was always considerate and compassionate in the extreme. No shadow of an ulterior motive crossed her mind.

Gast took Nietzsche six doughnuts every time that he visited. On 1st February, however, Nietzsche said, 'No, my friend, I do not want to get sticky fingers now because I want to play a little first. Then he sat down at the piano to improvise. Oh if only you had been listening! Not one wrong note! Interweaving tones of Tristan-like sensitivity! Pianissimo alternating with the fanfares of trumpets and the sonorous sound of trombones, Beethoven-like profundity with jubilant songs rising above it. Then again reveries and dreams. It beggars description! Oh for a phonograph!' So Gast took his leave of Nietzsche 'enormously strengthened in my belief we shall have our Nietzsche back again'.

There is even the hint that he may have been writing in secret. Here is his mother, 'He found a pencil and, as I had an old envelope, he began to write on it and was happy to be in his element. I could not prevent him from taking this pencil and another one out of the auditorium as well as paper which we finally discovered; and when I also said to him as a joke, "Old Fritz, you are really a little pack rat", he whispered in my ear as he took his leave quite cheerfully, "but now I will have something to do when I creep back into my burrow"'.

Indeed, one of the members of the staff at Jena, a Dr

Simchowitz, wrote of his personal talks with Nietzsche that he was astonished at the way in which the man spoke. He had never heard anything like it before and he tells us that, 'later when I read Nietzsche, it became clear to me what had puzzled me so much. For the first time I sensed the magical effect of the Nietzschian style. For he spoke just as he wrote. Terse sentences full of peculiar word combinations and ingenious antitheses; even the interspersed French and Italian phrases which he loved so much in his later writings were not missing. His manner had nothing of the professor or the lecturer about it'.

Which tallies with Overbeck's feelings when he came to Jena in February. After seeing his friend he wrote, 'I have always maintained that his madness, the beginning of which no one witnessed more closely than myself, was a misfortune as sudden as a flash of lightning. It came on between Christmas 1888 and Epiphany 1889'. Before this, in spite of his state of mental exaltation, Nietzsche cannot have been mad, 'Still, I will not lay that down as a hard and fast opinion, at times it has almost wavered, as I cannot escape the ghastly suspicion [...] that his madness is simulated. This impression can only be explained by the experiences I have had of Nietzsche's self-concealments, of his spiritual masks'.

Nietzsche to Overbeck, 'I have lost interest in everything. Deep down, an unyielding black depression and weariness too. I spend most of the time in bed [...] the worst of it is, I no longer see the point in living for even half a year more. Everything is boring, painful, dégoûtant, I have suffered and sacrificed too much; I feel so incomplete, so inexpressibly conscious of having bungled and botched my whole creative life. It is all hopeless. I will do nothing worthwhile again. Why do anything any more!'

And, writing of the Engadine to Carl von Gersdorff, 'For hearing my innermost voices it can never be too peaceful and high and lonely'.

To Rohde, 'I felt as if you were holding my hand and looking at me mournfully as if to say, "How can it be that

203

DAVID POLLARD

we now have so little in common, that we live in such different worlds" [...] It is all over, past history, merely a matter of being considerate. We still get together. But the truth can be seen in their eyes which say to me (I hear it well enough) "Nietzsche, you are now all alone"'.

To Overbeck again, 'My "philosophy" - if I have the right to give that name to that which tortures me to the very roots of my being - is no longer communicable, at least not in print'.

To Gast, on starting 'Ecce Homo', he wrote of, 'embarking on the frighteningly solitary act of revaluation'.

In 'Daybreak' Nietzsche wrote, 'Let us go one step further. All superior men who were irresistibly drawn to break apart the yoke of any morality and to give out new laws, if they were not actually mad, had no option but to make themselves, or pretend to be, mad. [...] "How can one make oneself mad when one is not and dare not appear mad?" - this terrible train of thought was followed by almost all the significant men of ancient civilisations; a secret teaching of artifice and dietetic hints was propagated on the subject together with the feeling that such reflections and purposes were innocent, even holy [...] Ah, give me madness, you heavenly powers! Madness, that at last I may believe in myself! Give deliriums and convulsions, sudden lights and darkness, terrify me with frost and fire such as no mortal has ever felt, with deafening noise and prowling forms, make me howl and whine and crawl like a beast only so that I may come to believe in myself!'

From 'Ecce Homo', 'To know thyself is the recipe for ruin [...] To become what one is, one must not have the faintest notion of what one is'.

Lou Salomé suggested that, 'Nietzsche's madness was integral to his thinking. He had experimented with himself as the subject for his thought for too long. The great thing that Nietzsche knew was that he was going under and yet with a laughing mouth he parted from life, absolving and justifying and transfiguring it'. And don't forget what Nietzsche had written about wisdom in 'The Gay Science', 'it is a screen behind which the philosopher can save himself when he becomes weary, old, cold, hard - when he feels that the end is near, like the instinctive wisdom animals have before their deaths: they go off by themselves, become still, choose solitude, hide in caves and become wise'.

In a letter to Gast, 'It is noble to regard solitude not as an option but as a given' and 'It is noble to have a resolute appearance of frivolity masking a stoic hardness and self-control'.

To Malwida von Meysenbug, 'This frightful and almost unremitting agony makes me hunger for the end and, judging by several indications, the cerebral coup-de-grace is close enough at hand to make me hopeful. As far as suffering and self-denial go I will match the last years of my life against those of any ascetic of any age'.

To Elizabeth in Paraguay, 'I take one sleeping pill after another to deaden the pain and for all that I cannot sleep. Today I will take such a dose that I lose my wits'.

To Strindberg, 'There is no question but that the hereditary criminal is decadent, even insane, But the history of criminal families [...] always leads one back to an individual who is too strong for his particular social environment. The latest major criminal case in Paris, Prado's, is a classic example. Prado was more than a match for his judges, even his lawyers, in self-control, wit and bravado. This is in spite of the fact that the pressure of the trial had already affected him so much physically that several witnesses recognised him only from old portraits'.

To Gast, 'My daily battle with headaches, together with the ridiculous assortment of ills that plagues me, demands so much attentiveness that I run the risk of becoming small-minded. But at least it serves to ballast the very general, very high-flying impulses which rule me to such a degree that without great counterweights I would surely go mad ... '

To Lou Salomé and Paul Rée, 'Even if some emotional

disturbance should happen to drive me to suicide, there wouldn't be all that much to mourn. Why should my fantasies concern you? (Even my "truths" haven't concerned you up to now). Do bear in mind that at bottom I am sick in the head and half insane, completely confused by long isolation'.

To Hans von Bülow, 'For years now I have lived somewhat too close to death and, what is worse, to pain. I seem designed for lengthy torment and skewering over a slow flame, and don't even know enough to lose my mind in the process'.

To Overbeck, 'I won't hide it from you; I am in a bad way. Darkness has closed in on me again [...] For a short time I was completely in my element, basking in my light. And now it is over. I believe I am surely done for unless something (I have no idea what) happens'.

Again that letter to Strindberg, 'I want, I want to be mad [...] It is a joy to be mad'.

Elizabeth, as expected, gave different reasons for her brother's insanity, 'Among the immediate causes [...] I include the enormous strain both on his intellect and on his short-sighted eyes. He worked extremely hard just before the onset of his madness' and she noted how exhausted he must have been. Thus, the stooping position which 'has an effect which injurs the nerves of the head and stomach and the terrible weather in the Engadine'. These 'brought on an attack of influenza which tormented him for weeks and had a very depressing effect'. It left behind an 'absurd insomnia which made him resort to sleeping draughts again'.

Then comes the real reason, 'I regard two sleeping draughts, chloral and Javanese narcotic, as responsible for his paralytic stroke'. She wrote that 'He used both of these in considerable quantities because he wanted to get through the enormous task before him'. The chloral was a help because it didn't leave him feeling weak the morning after using it. It also allowed him to sleep well and have pleasant dreams. She tells us he was worried by the habit but that the doctors assured him that it was harmless. However, she calls his taking it 'a very risky experiment'.

The Javanese narcotic was more of a problem. She wrote that he was introduced to it in 1884 by a Dutchman who 'presented him with a fairly large bottle of the specific. The stuff tasted like rather strong alcohol and had an outlandish smell. The Dutchman impressed on us the fact that only a few drops should be taken at a time in a glass of water'. It produced, according to Elizabeth, a false feeling of gaiety and made her brother 'suddenly throw himself on the ground in a fit of convulsive laughter'. This laughter, along with the grins and the forced gaiety, was a feature of his insanity. She concluded by writing that, 'during the early days of his insanity he used often to say in confidence to our mother that he "had taken twenty drops" (he did not mention of what) and that his brain had then "gone off the rails"'. She decided that 'the correct diagnosis, perhaps, would be that his brain had been exhausted by overstrain of the nerves of head and could no longer resist taking drugs to excess, and thus became disabled'.

Nietzsche wrote about 'The history of criminal families' thus, 'Wherever I seek my most profound opposite, that is, incalculable vulgarity of instinct, I always find my mother and sister. If I thought that I was in actual fact related to such canaille it would be a veritable blasphemy against my divinity. The treatment that I have always received from my mother and sister, up to the present moment, fills me with unutterable horror. Here a highly perfected, hellish machine is at work, one that operates with unfailing accuracy at the very moment that I am most vulnerable and likely to bleed [...] In these moments one lacks all the energy that would be needed to defend oneself against venomous vipers'.

207

At last he said with sadness, 'I know my fate. Well then! I am ready. My last solitude has just begun'.

'Ah, this sorrowful, black sea beneath me! Ah, this brooding reluctance! Ah, destiny and sea! Now I have to go down to you!'

'I stand before my highest mountain and my longest wandering therefore I must first descend deeper than I have ever descended - deeper into pain than I have ever descended, down to its blackest stream! My destiny will have it so. Well then! I am ready'.

What ceremony else?

Wagner is buried in the cemetery of Bayreuth near the grave of his father-in-law Liszt and his son-in-law Houston Stewart Chamberlain. Also nearby is the tomb of Winifred Wagner, buried with her husband Siegfried of the Idyll. She held artistic sway over the theatre while the Third Reich held sway over most of Europe. Just six years after the holocaust, when the Festspielhaus was reopened in 1951, a head of Wagner was carved and put on a pillar in a garden in Bayreuth not far from these graves. It is in the Nazi style and was carved by Arnold Preger. Who? He was Hitler's favourite sculptor.

In other less dignified graves are some other friends of Elizabeth's who had been hanged within an hour of each other in the gymnasium of the jail at Nuremberg: Ribbentrop, Keitel, Kaltenbrunner, Rosenberg, Frick, Seyss-Inquart, Franck and Sauckel who had read the funeral oration over the body of Elizabeth at the request of an influential friend. That friend, the dictator, was also dead and almost ready for resurrection. His charred body had mysteriously vanished never to return except for half a cranium with a bullet-hole through it that is now part of a touring exhibition.

Many who should have met their deaths at the hands of the hangman of Nuremberg were never captured or tried. Instead they made their way, with the connivance of the allies, the Church which worshipped another saviour of Europe and others in authority, to South America where they lived in some comfort for the most part and died (Eichmann excepted) in their beds.

Sightings are legion, not least in 'Nueva Germania' where every now and then, a figure leading a sad looking horse appears out of the jungle mists and makes its way to that overgrown, cracked gravestone and studies it intensely for a while, is invited to stay for a few days and sometimes does but then, invariably, vanishes again leaving nothing but vague talk of even vaguer similarities to...

No surprise at all to find that Nietzsche was read out during that trial at Nuremberg. Nazism, one of the prosecutors told the court, was the morality of immorality and the result of Nietzsche's purest teachings which regard the destruction of conventional morality to be the highest duty of man. Elizabeth had done her job thoroughly.

And at this point, perhaps, the eminence grise of the final solution inverts things in yet another kind of posthumous existence. In the diaries he wrote in jail, after his public trial in a Jerusalem theatre, Adolf (yes another one) Eichmann chose for his frontispiece a line from Plato's cave, that eerie Hades below ground where light from the upper world never filters, where illusion is the real and the real is an illusion, 'And he would consider his shadow world as real, but the real world as an illusion'. Those pieces of paper he shifted around his overneat desk so far away from anything real, where he was concerned only with the banality of a normal day at the office but where outside everything was inverted into its terrible opposite, into a reality which could not be conceived down there below ground. In his opinion his duties had nothing what-

209

ever to do with the actual, the acts, the actions of others and, where they did connect, he always sought the seal of the Gestapo chief, Heinrich Mueller. He had, as the high-ranking head of the Jewish Department, every right to command but made no use of it. In fact, his shadow world was real enough, that is shadowy enough, for many. Later Emil Fackenheim was to write that the Jew must accept and proclaim his Jewishness or, by assimilating and hiding in those very shadows through fear of recognition, he hands to Hitler another posthumous victory.

At the time, Buber stated that Eichmann should not have been hanged but should instead have been forced to work in the flourishing orchards of Israel among the Jews he would have had killed so that he could see each day how unfinal the solution had been and instead of death would have lived a posthumous existence.

And the figure whose footfalls have been crossing and recrossing the floor above us had become Nietzsche's phantom, a ghostly mirror image of the living man, so much more dead than simply lifeless. He had become the supreme exhibit of the archive which only the most special of guests were allowed to see. Just as Wagner had made a shrine to himself at Tribschen and Hitler had turned his rallies into living shrines to himself, so Elizabeth had built a shrine to her brother at Weimar. She dressed him in long, flowing robes that made him appear like an ancient Greek philosopher or a Catholic priest. It was their mother's faithful maid Alwyn who did the cooking and cleaning and sat with him all those endless hours while Elizabeth busied herself with her myth making beneath his feet. But it was Elizabeth who brought in the visitors and showed him off to the world. And she created yet another myth, the myth of her devotion to her brother. In her account Alwyn vanished and the nursing became her responsibility. One of the last things Nietzsche had written was to express the 'terrible fear that one day I shall be pronounced "holy"' and Elizabeth wrote as if in response 'His eventide was to me too holy!' She compared herself to the women around Socrates who were asked to leave because of their constant sobbing, because they cried and wailed, disturbing the thinker's repose in that Athenian prison. She was determined, so she said, not to be like them. She would protect the real Nietzsche from that kind of disturbance. Everything would be comfortable and well organised. Nothing for the philosopher to overcome. Nothing for him to write. No thinking. Elizabeth had taken those tasks to herself.

Already in 1897 Ferdinand Tinnies was writing, 'A philosophical writer who is read by many is already a remarkable thing. But suppose this writer should be read with enthusiasm, that readers should call themselves disciples, that his thought should be received as an emancipation and a revelation, that these people should feel that in the thinker they had found a Führer'.

No longer a man, it took only one further small step to turn him into a god. Rudolph Steiner wrote what he was thinking as he worked on the documents downstairs, 'He sat enthroned on the veranda above in solemn awfulness, unconcerned with us, like a god of Epicurus. Whoever saw Nietzsche at this time as he reclined in his white pleated robe, with the glance of a Brahman in his wide and deep-set eyes, beneath bushy eyebrows, with the nobility of his enigmatic, questioning face and the leonine, majestic carriage of his thinker's head, had the impression that this man could not die, but that his eye would rest for all eternity upon mankind. This man, the thinker who had had the temerity to kill the gods and have done with all the immortals on Parnassus, had been placed there by their sides'. What he had overcome had itself been overcome and the dead had been brought to life. Lazarus had been raised from the dead and returned to life inverted, had been taken from life and returned

211

before his time to immortality and been given back his death. What a myth by which to judge all the myths of the future.

One of those allowed up the hallowed staircase into the presence of the living corpse was the Baroness van Unger-Sternberg and she saw 'all the loftiness and beauty of his soul shining through his form!' She writes of the beauty of his eyes, of those eyes which had caused the living writer so much pain. She sees them 'no longer veiled by spectacles, as simply overpowering. Those deep-set, melancholy, star-like eyes, that seemed to rove the distance and yet to look within'. Those eyes exerted a magnetic influence. How carefully had the stage been set, and the visitor prepared. The archive as church to the new god and the staircase as steps to the altar. To destroy the creativity of the gods is one thing and can only be done through the mouth of a madman. This Nietzsche understood while he was still a man. But to recreate the gods again in your own image, to make of the holy nothing more than another myth, for this you need a madman who has given up even his madness and can himself be turned into something holy.

'Holy, Holy, Holy is the lord of ghosts'.

And even Lou von Salomé had written that, 'He parted from his life, absolving, justifying and transfiguring it'. Not unlike another Salomé who ordered the death of another god-like figure or the other Salomé who, after weeping over another kind of lingering death, went to another tomb with spices to anoint a god but fled from the place.

And what was it that Lou's lover, Rilke, had written about that wax figure of Christ in a booth at the Munich Fair, about the dead being martyred for their very lack of faith, about the wandering Jew in quite another shape. The figure on the cross whose final words had spoken of his loss of faith and of his death without belief, who looked down on the poet and spoke:

This is my curse
Since my disciples robbed my grave of me,
Deluded by their proud and boastful faith,
There is no pit can hold me - none.
So long as rushing steams reflect the stars
And life bursts forth under an April sun,
I must go on and on across the earth,
And pay my penance now from cross to cross

Know you the legend of the Wandering Jew?
I am myself that ancient Ahasvar
Who daily dies and daily lives anew.

As Disraeli wrote, 'Over every altar [...] we find the tables of the Jewish Law', above a writhing figure of the Jewish Christ, a flying Dutchman, a wandering Jew, forced to live in exile against his most ardent wishes.

We have the final moment from Elizabeth. On Monday August 20th he suddenly caught a feverish cold and his breathing became more and more difficult. There was a real risk that he would get an inflammation of the lungs. This risk persisted for a few days, but, with the help of the doctor, it seemed that the danger had passed. Yet, just before midday four days later, while Elizabeth was sitting opposite him his whole expression changed suddenly and, seized with a paralytic stroke, he dropped back unconscious. As this happened a terrible storm began outside as if Friedrich was trying to die in the midst of thunder and lightning (There is no mention of the raiment of the Temple). However, he came round again and even made an effort to speak to her.

The end came towards two o'clock the following night. Elizabeth was moving the lampshade to one side in order to hand him a refreshing draught when he looked at her

213

and cried our her name joyfully, '"Elizabeth" was the last word that passed his lips for now his beloved face began to change little by little and his breathing became more and more of an effort and the shadow of death began to spread across his features'. For the last time he opened his glorious eyes to gaze upon her and opened and closed his lips once or twice as if he still had something to say but could say nothing. Then there was a slight shudder, a deep sigh and softly, without any struggle, with one final glance in her direction, he closed his eyes forever. 'Such was the passing of Zarathustra'.

The footfalls are hardly audible through the thick boards of the first floor ceiling yet, nonetheless, are still resounding through this enormous story. If you could be silent for a moment and even stop the rustling of those documents, maybe hold your breath ... Yes there they are - one two three four five six seven wheel one two three four five six seven wheel. The shuffling of slippers to and fro. The padding back and forth of a great thinker for whom music was an abiding passion. This ghostly shuffling is all that remains of such heroic love of music - a tuneless pulse, a shadowy heartbeat - one two three four five six seven wheel one two three four five six seven wheel. Will you not try to snatch a little sleep?

And the Maestro, of course, resurrected art after it had taken a long sleep. Nietzsche was 'a disciple of art resurrected'. The birth, no the rebirth, of tragedy out of the spirit of music and the rebirth also of the "aesthetically responsive spectator"'.

'As far as suffering and self-denial go I will match the last years of my life against those of any ascetic of any age'. 'Ah, give me madness, you heavenly powers! Madness, that I may at last believe in myself! Give deliriums and convulsions, sudden lights and darkness, terrify me with frost and fire such as no mortal has ever felt, with deafening noise and prowling forms, make me howl and whine and crawl like a beast so that I may only come to believe in myself!'

'The patience of the scream has no limits. It outlasts martyrdom' wrote Edmund Jabès.

And other bodies which were transformed into shapes of a different kind, 'a habitual feeling of my real life having past and that I am leading a posthumous existence'. 'A little later, when he was quite forgotten, she began to - A little later, when as though he had never been, it had never been, she began to - 'From the mythic nonsense of this so loving sister and her archive, her museum with its living, breathing exhibit, footfalls of the dead. He is in his Hades just above the floorboards.

And who was it who said, 'I cannot escape the ghastly suspicion [...] that his madness is simulated. This impression can only be explained by the experiences I have had of his self-concealments, of his spiritual masks?' Yes, Overbeck, the friend who was so grateful for the moment of recognition he had received in that railway carriage, the man he had loved most of all, the man who knew that this was no longer his friend but another man, a mask, a mystery.

'I felt as if you were holding my hand and looking at me mournfully as if to say, "How can it be that we have so little in common now, that we live in such different worlds?" Yet at one time - And this is how it is with everyone I care about, 'It is all over, past history, merely a matter of being considerate. We still get together. But the truth can be seen in their eyes which say to me (I hear it well enough) "You are now all alone"'.

'Now all profane books are odious to me and I understand my folly and the peril I have received from reading them'. They had understood nothing of what he had written when he was as sane as any man but now that he was clearly mad the relief in their faces when they realised

215

that they had understood that he was making no sense whatsoever was manifest. Now, at last, they were on safe ground. The incomprehensibility of the sane was a problem but that of a madman they could deal with. Elizabeth's job was to resurrect a kind of sanity out of this madness even though he had told her, 'You wish to sacrifice your life, not to my lofty aims but to the ideals which I have got beyond and must now fight against'.

Now that they all understood at last that he was both a dying man and mad they fell to their knees and begged him not to die, 'for the maddest thing that a man may do in this life is to let himself die just like that, without anyone killing him'. But he answered, 'Let us go gently for there are no birds this year in last year's nest. I was mad but now I am sane'.

Another metamorphosis, 'As he opened the door he thought I've an idea I don't grow any older now, and when I come to die, it'll seem an odd, out-of-date sort of catastrophe. Hardly was he well inside his room when the door was hastily shut, bolted and locked. The sudden noise in his rear startled him so much that his little legs gave way beneath him. It was his sister who had shown such haste. She had been standing ready waiting and had made a light spring forward, he had not even heard her coming and she cried out At last! as she turned the key in the lock'.

The grave is as good a place to close as any and, like so many other things in this story, it is not as is seems for it is just possible that those three bodies in their small plot in the churchyard at Röcken are not directly beneath their gravestones.

Elizabeth had a tombstone prepared for herself which matched her brother's exactly and she was careful to leave a gap for her own coffin between those of her brother and mother thus reserving for herself, in death as in life, a central place. There is a rumour to the effect that she was forced to shift her brother's headstone a metre or more to the left to make enough space for her own. If the rumour is true, then Elizabeth's headstone is, at least partly, above the body of her brother. A metaphor in solid stone if ever we should need one .